GREY KNIGHTS

THE INCORRUPTIBLE

CONTENTS

PRODUCED BY GAMES WORKSHOP IN NOTTINGHAM

With thanks to the Mournival for their additional playtesting services

British Cataloguing-in-Publication Data. A catalogue record for this book is available from the British Library.

Games Workshop Ltd, Willow Rd, Lenton, Nottingham, NG7 2WS
games-workshop.com

INTRODUCTION

You hold in your hands a most sanctified tome of lore: the definitive guide to the elite Daemon-hunting order known as the Grey Knights. This book will help you to assemble your collection of Grey Knights Citadel Miniatures into a powerful tabletop army, bound together by military structure and guided by noble heraldry and ancient lore.

The Grey Knights are one of the most elite armies in the Warhammer 40,000 galaxy. They are a force of individuals, a company of heroes in which every model is a powerful addition to your force. As the Imperium's ultimate answer to the daemonic menace, the Grey Knights are permitted enormous autonomy to deploy whatever warriors and weapons will best answer any given threat. In collecting and gaming terms, this permits you freedom to build whatever force you like, from whichever models appeal to you the most. Whether you assemble a conclave of the Chapter's greatest heroes, a gleaming armoured spearhead of blessed silver battle tanks, a questing formation of Dreadknights, or an entire brotherhood ready for war, *Codex: Grey Knights* contains all the rules and information you need to bring your army to life on the tabletop.

Building and painting Grey Knights is a unique and exciting challenge for collectors of any ability. Every model in a Grey Knights army is a lavishly detailed individual piece, whether it is a courageous hero, elite warrior or venerable war engine. Even the largest squads of Grey Knights never number more than ten models, meaning you have a force in which every miniature can be treated as its own project, with personalised heraldry, unique honour badges, stunning weaponry, and as great a level of detail as you choose to apply.

Within this book you will find all the information you need to collect a Grey Knights army and field it upon the tabletop.

THE EMPEROR'S GIFT: This section gives a comprehensive account of the Grey Knights' history, and their ongoing duties in service to the Emperor. It also provides an in-depth analysis of how their armies organise themselves and fight in battle.

THE 666th CHAPTER: Here you will find a showcase of beautifully painted miniatures showing the heraldry of the Grey Knights and example armies to inspire your own collection.

THE ARMY OF TITAN: This section includes datasheets, wargear lists and weapon rules for every Grey Knights unit and model for you to use in your games.

THE HAMMER OF DAEMONS: This section provides additional rules, including Warlord Traits, Stratagems, Relics and psychic powers, as well as matched play points, that allow you to transform your collection of miniatures into a purifying Grey Knights army.

To play games with your army, you will need a copy of the Warhammer 40,000 rules. To find out more about Warhammer 40,000 or download the free core rules, visit games-workshop.com.

ET TEMPLARS MYSTERIA AUX ORDO MALLEUS

Praise the Emperor for his sacrifice,
as He endures so shall we.
We who are Hunters of Daemons,
shall strive in his name eternally.

We the Order of the Hammer,
shall delve into the Dark Shadows.
We shall seek out the Tainted,
we shall pursue the Vilest Evil.

It is we who stand guard,
our Eternal Watch shall not fail.
For we are the Ordo Malleus!

We Grey Knights are the Hammers,
we slay the Darkness without fear.
Founded in great mystery we were,
Chapter six hundred and sixty six.

Though on Titan we be hidden,
yet our eyes encompass the Galaxy.
No Devil shall elude our gaze,
no Daemon shall avoid its Fate.

We shall be the Keepers Immortal,
all Secrets shall be our Knowledge.
We are the Guardians of Mankind!

Caution and secrecy are our code,
watchfulness and patience are our way.
Hidden from the Eyes of Chaos,
we strike without warning or dread.

Though we find ourselves in Shadows,
no Blackness will enter our Hearts.
No treachery will touch our souls,
no pride will sully our thoughts.

We shall be Pure amongst Impurity,
we shall be Innocence amongst Guilt.
We are the Imperium's Hidden Saviours!

We are spread across the Heavens,
our watch is untiring and ceaseless.
The Emperor shall guard our Souls,
as we Guard those of others.

Our will shall be our weapons,
our faith shall be our armour.
Our minds will be secure fortresses,
no Temptation will weaken our resolve.

Though unnumbered lurking perils await
us, our blades will ever be ready.
For we are the Emperor's Vengeance!

Masters of all weapons are we,
no defence exists against our wrath.
With the Nemesis shall we fight,
with an Aegis to shield us.

In bloodshed shall we save Mankind,
Death shall be our Everlasting Creed.
War Unending shall be our Fate,
in battle shall we be steeped.

We shall be unstinting in Hatred,
we shall hunger for Holy War.
For we are Swords of Justice!

When all flee in hideous disarray,
strong and sound shall we stand.
Cowardice is wholly unknown to us,
our courage comes from the Emperor.

Unbowed and unshaken against all foes,
we shall claim victory with blood.
Steady and surely we hunt them,
those that dare oppose our wrath.

Death stalks us in many forms,
the grotesque and the utterly inhuman.
We are the Bringers of Hope!

Bloody battles unending constantly
await us, redemption the reward for
our vigilance.
When Possession rears its unspeakable head,
ours is the blade that descends.

When Empyrean Horrors invade our
realm, our Exorcisms shall hurl them back.
There is no Chaos spawned horror,
which can resist our indomitable anger.

With undaunted courage we shall prevail,
no arcane magicks shall overcome us.
We are the Bearers of Victory!

No corruption shall blemish our Galaxy,
no Immaterial Fiend shall be spared.
No Malevolent Spirit will oppose us,
no Creation of Sin shall survive.

No Unholy Deed shall go Unpunished,
all Blasphemous Acts shall be Atoned.
No Spawn of Misrule avoids us,
all are banished to the Void.

Nothing shall evade our Cleansing Fire,
not Daemon or Spawn or Renegade.
For we are Mankind's Divine Blade!

Heavenly Blessings are laid upon us,
the Warp is ours to Tame.
Though Sorceries shall be against us,
no Witchcraft will bring our Doom.

Though Spell or Incantation blocks us,
the Emperor shall see us Victorious.
No Hex can overcome our determination,
our resolve is strong as steel.

Sigils and wards watch over us,
prayers shall serve as our Guide.
For we are the Emperor's Chosen!

There is much darkness awaiting us,
yet the Emperor lights our path.
Falsehood surrounds us at every turn,
yet no Traitor shall confound us.

No despicable trickery will thwart us,
no Damnation shall bring us low.
There is no peace for us,
for an eternity we will strive.

Though mere mortals in His service,
everlasting shall be our True Duty.
Et Imperator Invocato Diabolus
Daemonica Exorcism!

The Canticle of Absolution of the Grey Knights, known as
The Six Hundred and Sixty-Six Secret Words. Source: corrupted datafile 0/223/Inq\6a

THE EMPEROR'S GIFT

The Grey Knights are the most mysterious of all the Imperium's many organisations. Few outside the upper echelons of the Inquisition hold any knowledge of the Chapter's founding, and even these most trusted of men are denied the full truth.

According to legend, the Grey Knights first appeared during the tumult of the Second Founding, when the nine loyalist Space Marine Legions were divided into the Chapters of today. Designated Chapter 666, the Grey Knights appeared amongst the growing roster of Space Marines, but would forever stand apart from their fellows. Where the Chapters of the Second Founding were but the reorganisation of what had gone before, the Grey Knights were something altogether new, the culmination of a project begun by the Emperor during the final days of the Horus Heresy.

As Horus' final campaign began, the Emperor foresaw that the end of the Heresy would cost him greatly, so much so that he would no longer be able to take an active hand in Mankind's survival – if he even survived at all. Yet he also knew that the threat of Chaos would not see defeat with Horus, but would continue to haunt humanity. Who then would defend Mankind against the Chaos Gods and their Daemons? The very nature of the Horus Heresy had proven that the Space Marines were not immune to corruption as the Emperor had once hoped. The loyal Custodes were still untouched by taint, but lacked the freedom of will that would be so essential in the coming battle.

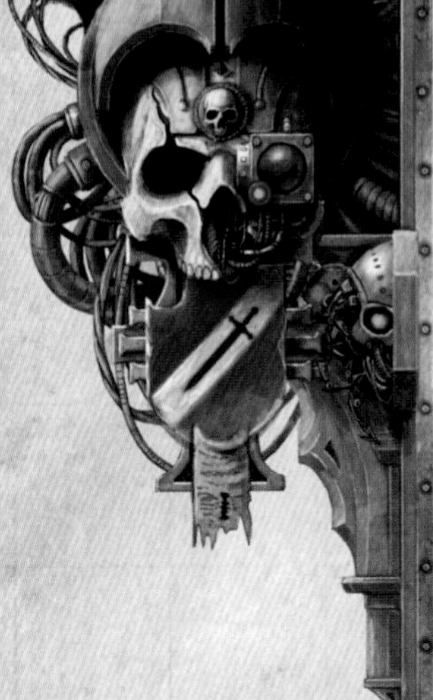

So did the Emperor set his hand to plans that would win a wider victory from the ashes of a most personal defeat. Malcador the Sigillite, closest of the Emperor's servants, scoured the battle-torn worlds of the Imperium for the men upon whose shoulders the burden of the future would be placed. No easy task would this have been in the calm of peace, but amidst the anarchy of the Horus Heresy it was almost impossible. By the time Malcador returned to his Emperor, Terra itself was under siege, and only through the most artful of subterfuge were the Sigillite and his recruits able to pass unscathed through the battle lines and come unharmed and unseen before the Emperor.

In stern silence the Emperor surveyed the robed figures that Malcador had brought before him, and he saw that his faithful servant had done well. Of the twelve, four were lords and administrators possessed of inquisitive nature and unyielding strength of mind. The other eight were Space Marines whose abilities were as peerless as their dedication to the Emperor. Some hailed from Legions that had abandoned the Emperor's light in favour of Horus' dark promises, but these battle-brothers had never lost their loyalty and had fought the Heresy from within. Fulsome in his approval of the selection, the Emperor bade Malcador proceed with the next stage of his plan.

TITAN

So dismissed, Malcador and the twelve departed the embattled palace as unremarked as they had arrived. Yet when the group departed Terra they divided, for their destinies would be separate for a time. The four lords left to lay the framework of the Inquisition – that mighty and secretive organisation charged with keeping watch over all arms of the Imperium – while Malcador took the eight Space Marines to the moon of Titan. Through sorcerous means, the Sigillite had long ago shielded the moon from the sight and deeds of loyalists and traitors alike. There the eight Space Marines discovered a fortress monastery prepared for them, founded in desperate secrecy beneath Malcador's shield of illusion. Contained within the fortress walls they would find everything necessary to create a new army of Space Marines: the Grey Knights. Suitable recruits had been gathered from across the span of the galaxy; some were raw and untrained, others selected in secret from the ranks of those Space Marine Legions that had remained loyal. New supplies of gene-seed lay preserved in cryovaults, and fresh-forged armaments stood ready in cloistered armouries. Theirs would not be a Space Marine Legion, but a Chapter – a smaller, more tightly knit brotherhood, but one with numbers enough for the task at hand.

Malcador supervised the initial creation of the Grey Knights, but he could not remain to oversee their evolution, so selected one of the eight to lead the Chapter in the years to come. So did Janus become the first Supreme Grand Master – the hand that would guide the Grey Knights through their early challenges. Before leaving Titan for the final time, Malcador forged one last enchantment, greater than any that had come before it. Titan vanished completely from its orbit, hidden from Horus in the most unlikely of refuges – Malcador had

'The Daemon has many forms. You must know them all. You must tell the Daemon from his disguise and root him out from the hidden places. Trust no one. Trust not even yourself. It is better to die in vain than to live in abomination. The zealous martyr is praised for his valour, the craven and the unready are justly abhorred.'

- Excerpt from The First Book of Indoctrinations

anchored it amongst the tides of the warp. Protected by Macro-Geller fields and sigilic rites of Malcador's own devising, Titan rode out the tumult of the warp whilst the rest of the galaxy endured through the last months of the Horus Heresy and the tragedy of the Emperor's final battle.

THE RETURN

Titan finally returned to its orbit in the mortal realm amidst the anarchy of the Second Founding. Time had flowed differently in the warp, and Titan had endured a measure of years far greater than the time that had passed in realspace. So it was that a Chapter that had entered the warp composed of a mere eight Space Marines and hundreds upon hundreds of untrained recruits, emerged with a full complement of one thousand fully trained battle-brothers.

At this time, the mighty Space Marine Legions were in the process of being separated into Chapters according to the precepts of the Codex Astartes. Much of the process of the Second Founding was being carried out at the direction of the newly formed Inquisition and was in turn overseen by those same lords who had left Terra with Malcador some years earlier. It was a simple task for them to include the Grey Knights amongst the growing roster of Space Marine Chapters, bestowing upon them the designation Chapter 666 – an oddity, as at the time, there were barely four hundred Space Marine Chapters commissioned. Few other details ever became a matter of record, and most of these were erased from the archives within a century.

Where the other Space Marine Chapters would be autonomous, the Grey Knights were fully embedded in the Inquisition, and would serve as the chamber militant of that most secret of societies. Where the other Space Marine Chapters were built upon existing stock, the Grey Knights were born of a new gene-seed, one without the flaws of those that had gone before, and which carried the gift of the Emperor's own flesh and soul. So was each Grey Knight a doughty warrior, his strength and endurance increased well beyond human limitations by the Emperor's gift and then honed further by rigorous training. Even unarmed and unarmoured, a lone Grey Knight would prove a hardy and difficult foe – but the Grey Knights seldom fight singly, and never without their weapons of war.

And such weapons of war! Even in the closing years of the 41st Millennium no army in all the Imperium can boast wargear so technologically advanced, so irrefutably sacred or so fearfully revered as that housed within the armouries of the Grey Knights. Such is the fruit borne of ancient pacts with the Adeptus Mechanicus, and even certain alien factions spread throughout the galaxy – so dire is the peril of Daemons that even considerations of race have been put aside. These are alliances of convenience against the daemonic threat – temporary confluences of goals and survival – rather than lasting bonds, and the technological legacy will doubtless long outlast the accords by which it was forged.

WARRIORS AND SORCERERS

Yet advanced technology is the least of the weapons in the Grey Knights' armoury. Daemons are not creatures of science, but beings of the darkest myth and madness. To battle such monsters and emerge victorious, a warrior must be steeped in that same madness; he must embrace the sorceries of the warp and so battle the Daemon with its own weapons. No ordinary human psyker could hope to do this, for even the attempt would ravage their unguarded mind, or – worse yet – open a portal from which the foul denizens of the warp could pour forth. Yet a Grey Knight can not only endure such trials, but thrive amongst them. His strength lies not in martial might alone, but also in his mind.

The Grey Knights are the inheritors and wardens of the Imperium's deepest knowledge of the warp. The Chapter as a whole is tasked with walking the razor-thin line that lies between psychic empowerment and absolute corruption. To this end, each battle-brother is an accomplished psyker, trained to channel his mental energies into the halo of protective wards known as the Aegis, and an array of formidable battle-powers. A Grey Knight's psychic presence is anathema to creatures of the warp, utterly unpalatable to a Daemon's dark appetites and thus entirely immune from corruption. Such was the Emperor's gift to the very first Grey Knights; a legacy renewed in each new generation of battle-brothers. Thus armoured, a Grey Knight can wield forbidden sorceries, harness tainted artefacts and scour the pages of blasphemous tomes without risk of being overwhelmed by the cursed power at his command.

There are those amongst the ranks of Grey Knights who are so powerful that their psychic essence cannot be completely contained by ritual or training. In any other warrior, this flow of escaping energy would prove an irresistible lure to Daemons, and the psyker be instantaneously corrupted to their vile desires. However, such is a Grey Knight's sanctity of soul that his psychic energy is unpalatable to all but the most ravenous of warp entities. This untainted energy takes a form dictated by the Grey Knight's subconscious mind – a cleansing flame, a burst of blinding light, or some other such physical manifestation of spiritual purity. The mightiest Grey Knights of all can banish Daemons with but a touch, restore courage in armies driven mad with terror, or even render themselves immune to the ravages of death itself.

NAMES OF POWER

No Grey Knight bears the name he was given at his birth. This is in part to distance him from his previous life and loyalties – an outward sign of having essentially been reborn in the service of the Inquisition. In any case, once a Grey Knight's identity has been broken down and rebuilt during training, he is unlikely to remember his past, so what matter if his name is no longer what it was? Only on completion of training is a Grey Knight granted his new name – until that point recruits are assigned only a number. Each name is actually a fragment of magical lore, divined by the labours of the Chapter's scribes to act in perfect opposition to the true name of a particular Daemon. Thus, even the Grey Knight's name is a weapon against his hated foe.

Like the true names of Daemons, the auspicious names given to Grey Knights are ever in flux. Nonetheless, some have resurfaced again and again over the millennia, gaining in power just as a specific Daemon is reborn from the warp. So it is that a Grey Knight's name might have been borne by many battle-brothers before him. Each name carries with it the history and deeds of those who have held it before, and amongst Daemons is a word of great power and terror.

THE CITADEL OF TITAN

For almost one hundred centuries, Titan has been the secret fortress of the Grey Knights. Glittering in the darkness of Saturn's shadow, the ice moon bristles with orbital defence platforms and fleets of sleek grey vessels. Beneath its frozen surface generations of Grey Knights are created and laid to rest, in an eternal cycle of service to the Imperium.

On Saturn's moon of Titan, nestled in the shadow of Mount Anarch, the fortress monastery of the Grey Knights juts from the ice sheets and oceans of liquid methane like a jagged black spire. Long has this fortress stood. Its dusty, echoing halls are hung with battle honours stretching back almost ten thousand years, though few outside the Chapter would recognise the names of the conflicts inscribed in the faded gold lettering. This mighty structure, designed to accommodate over a thousand Space Marines and all their weapons of war, stands largely silent and empty. The daemonic threat can strike anywhere across the galaxy and, in opposing that threat, most of the Grey Knights are scattered throughout the stars. Only in the Chamber of Trials, where the unceasing work of recruitment and training is carried out, does clamour reign. Elsewhere, the Grey Knights go about their duties in silent meditation, their thoughts bent upon their unending mission.

THE CHAMBER OF TRIALS

It is from the Chamber of Trials that the Gatherers set out across the galaxy in search of recruits. The Gatherers are Grey Knights whose great age or severe injuries no longer permit them to undertake the primary work of the Chapter, but whose keen senses and minds can still detect an aspirant hero amongst the common rabble of Humanity. There is no limit to the Gatherers' remit. Whilst most Space Marine Chapters recruit from only a handful of worlds, the Grey Knights' Gatherers can induct from any world in the Imperium – though their preference is ever for the barbaric worlds that necessitate physical and mental toughness from birth. Should they wish, the Gatherers can even recruit directly from the Black Ships – the ghostly vessels that prowl the Imperium, gathering tithes of psykers – or from the selection grounds of other Space Marine Chapters. Indeed, some Chapters, notably the Exorcists and the Silver Skulls, take it upon themselves to identify those amongst their own recruits in whom the Grey Knights might show an interest and notify the Gatherers directly. As a Space Marine Chapter lives or dies by its ability to replenish losses, for one to willingly give up a part of its intake to another is an honourable gift indeed, a sign of the respect in which the Grey Knights are held by those few who know of them.

The Chamber of Trials is where aspirants arrive and their training begins. A continuous stream of shuttles flit about its spires, bringing in fresh cargoes of recruits or leaving with the bodies of the slain. During approach and departure each vessel is tracked closely by a pair of the fortress monastery's defence lasers. The slightest deviation from the designated flight lanes is met automatically with twin lances of scarlet energy that instantly turn the most heavily defended transports into lifeless meteors of fused slag.

'Abandon compassion and pity. They will not aid you in this war. Your soul is the crucible, and hatred your only weapon against the Daemon. Let both burn bright.' - Prognosticar Theoddus, vision from the Augurium.

The Chapter's initial training process is necessarily harsh, for it must swiftly weed out those who do not have the fortitude to become a Grey Knight. The Emperor's gift is much too rare and valuable to risk wasting. Only one in a thousand candidates survives the first rite of passage, the pilgrimage through the haunted plains of Xanadu Regio, and most of these will be slain in the second – the trek through the pitch-black, Glyphite-stalked caverns beneath Ganesa Macula. All told, perhaps one in a million novitiates makes it through the full gamut of physical and mental challenges to be deemed worthy of receiving the Emperor's gift and beginning the transformation from human to Grey Knight.

The physical changes of becoming a Grey Knight are accomplished in the lowermost levels of the chamber, where a warren of psycho-surgeries and bio-engineering chambers are watched over by tireless arrays of Servitors. Once these procedures are complete, the novitiate is ordained as a neophyte and his true training begins – his martial skills developed at the hands of the Brotherhood Champions, and his psychic powers honed by the Chapter's Librarians. Most important of all, he must perform the many Rituals of Detestation that will harden his heart against the whispered temptations of Chaos and the honeyed lies of Daemons. To wade in the stuff of damnation and walk away without the slightest blemish on the soul requires the most resolute will and the purest heart. Should these final challenges be met and passed, the neophyte will be raised to the rank of Knight.

THE AUGURIUM

The silver pinnacle that is the Chapter Augurium lies at the top of the fortress monastery's tallest tower. Within its mirrored walls, the Grey Knights' Prognosticars go about their rituals and meditations, illuminated only by the dim light of guttering candles. Prognosticars are powerful, highly specialised psykers, who are particularly sensitive to fluctuations in the warp and who read psychic tremors to predict the location and severity of forthcoming daemonic incursions. Whilst the skills of the Prognosticars might seem oracular in form, in function they are much more akin to highly specialised hunting instincts, tracking the unholy spoor of Daemons through the roiling tides of the immaterium as a predator stalks its prey.

Forewarned by the Prognosticars, the Grey Knights can deploy their forces according to the nature of the threat at hand, rather than relying on delayed or misleading reports from a battle zone. Though such predictions are prone to a certain amount of inaccuracy, the Prognosticars provide the Chapter with a level of foresight without which its mission would be all but impossible. If a Grey Knight commander orders the destruction of a passenger liner to ensure the banishment of a single Daemon hidden aboard, he does not do so out of callousness, but out of pragmatism. Thanks to the warnings of the Prognosticars he knows, where others cannot, that the escape of that Daemon would lead to the damnation of far more souls than those that perished in the liner's destruction. In the Grey Knights' war against the Daemons, the tally of the slain can only ever increase – all the Sons of Titan can do is moderate the collateral damage. If millions must be sacrificed to save billions, then so be it.

CHAMBERS OF PURITY

The Chapter's legends tell that a great evil lies entombed amongst the roots of Mount Anarch, although its true nature is shrouded in mystery. It is uncertain whether this was the reason that Titan was chosen as the Chapter Planet for the Grey Knights – so that the entrammelled evil should ever have watchful and incorruptible guardians – or if something defeated Malcador's defences and crept onto Titan during the moon's time in the warp. The truth lies only in the Iron Grimoire – the Grey Knights' sole written record of their founding, a tome inked with the blood of saints and bound in screaming warp-metal. Only a Supreme Grand Master is permitted to read this tome, and it would be unthinkable for one to share its contents with his own battle-brothers, let alone outsiders.

The Iron Grimoire likens the rock of Titan to a graven tomb, and the Chambers of Purity – the oldest part of the citadel – to its capstone. It is here that the Purifiers, noblest of the Grey Knights, are quartered, and few outsiders are permitted within. Only the Purifiers know the exact nature of their prisoner, and they do not speak of it, not even to the Grand Masters of the Chapter. Yet when the rock of Titan shakes and the Purifiers seal the approaches to their chambers, the Chapter holds its collective breath until the tremors end and the obsidian doors are opened once again.

THE DEAD FIELDS

It is the fervent wish of every Grey Knight that upon his death he be carried back to Titan to be interred in the consecrated crypts of the Dead Fields. In these vaults have the honoured dead been laid to rest since the earliest days of the Chapter, their likenesses preserved in bas-relief and lit with azure flames. Before a battle-brother is interred, his body is cleansed and the six hundred and sixty-six words of sanctity are inscribed upon his skin. His armour and weapons are returned to the Chapter's armoury, though the heraldry of the fallen Grey Knight is often etched onto them in recognition of his deeds.

All too often, however, a battle-brother's body is lost forever to the tides of war and cannot be set in its rightful place in the Dead Fields. If no body is available, then the warrior's name will be recorded in honour on the chamber's great basalt wall of remembrance, there to echo through eternity alongside the very greatest of the Chapter's heroes.

THE TERMINUS DECREE

Deep within the Chambers of Purity, locked away in the chamber said to hold the tomb of the Sigillite himself, rests a simple wooden box, embellished with a golden seal. Within this box, written upon ancient parchment, is the instruction known only as the Terminus Decree. This artefact goes unrecorded in all the libraries of the Imperium, for it has been kept secret from all but the Supreme Grand Masters of the Chapter.

Only a Supreme Grand Master of the Grey Knights knows how to open the box, and he will do so only when all hope for the future of Humanity seems lost. The Terminus Decree is the ultimate sanction of the Grey Knights, a secret so vast it could bring the Imperium to its knees, or save it in its darkest hour.

The exact nature of the document is unknown, and the only clue to its contents lies in the box's golden seal. It is whispered that it is the exact match of another seal, found only in one place in all the Imperium's many scattered worlds: the Emperor's Golden Throne.

HALL OF CHAMPIONS

The Hall of Champions is the seat of the Paladins – the Grey Knights' greatest warriors. Rank upon rank of marble statues line the walls, each bearing the likeness of a mighty hero from the Chapter's past; a Paladin, a Brother-Captain or a Grand Master granted graven immortality so that he may inspire the generations of Grey Knights yet to come.

In such auspicious company are the Chapter's feast days held, beneath vaulted rafters laden with trophies seized upon the field of battle: weapons, banners, armour fragments and artefacts so unusual as to be unrecognisable. Few of these trophies are daemonic in nature – rather they are victory tokens captured from mortal foes. Though the Grey Knights are principally concerned with the daemonic menace, they have fought countless battles against the alien, the mutant and the heretic, and the trophies in the Hall of Champions stand as testament to these victories.

Most warp-spawned prizes are instead locked away in the deepest vaults. The one notable exception is the charred skull of Iremn'ath, the Daemon Rajah of Nalu, whose repeated assaults on the Ibb worldmaze led the Grey Knights into one of their longest and costliest campaigns. Now Iremn'ath's cursed spirit is doomed to dwell above the Grand Masters' high table in a prison of his own skull, caged by the ceaseless chanting of three score acolytes who exist only to see that the hexagrammic wards that cage him never fail. For the Grey Knights, the skull of Iremn'ath represents a shard of hope that final victory against the Daemons is not impossible. For Iremn'ath, it is the most bitter of punishments. Unable to escape, he must watch the Grey Knights celebrate their every triumph, raging silently and impotently against his downfall.

In our quest to stem the Daemon tide there is no price we shall not pay, no sacrifice too great. If we must extinguish the light of a trillion souls each day to safeguard this Imperium, we shall gladly be about the task. To do aught else would be heresy.

THE SANCTUM SANCTORUM

In many ways, this chamber is the heart of the Grey Knights Chapter, for it contains the accumulated knowledge of their long history, as well as many rare gems of lore garnered from the Emperor's own experiences in the long millennia before that. Herein are recorded the rituals and procedures of the myriad psychic abilities that the Grey Knights call upon, as well as several closely guarded secrets concerning the crafting of Nemesis force weapons, the forging of new Grey Knights and some of the other technologies unique to the Chapter.

In the darkest chamber of the Sanctum Sanctorum lies the Librarium Daemonica – the Grey Knights' repository of knowledge concerning all things daemonic. Twisting corridors of age-worn oaken cabinets fill this heavily guarded library, their shelves bowed under the weight of crumbling scrolls, gnarled tomes and occasional clusters of tarnished and blackened datacrystals. The threat of such knowledge falling into the wrong hands is taken very seriously indeed, and it is said that nowhere in the Imperium, save the Emperor's Palace itself, is as well protected as this unholy chamber. It lies behind three sets of adamantium walls, each a barricade several yards thick, protected by sigillite enchantments scribed in languages long dead, anointed with consecrated oils and inscribed with silver seals of warding. The only way to reach the library's heart is to pass through the three portals – the first is a cipher-locked blast door, the second a spatial displacement field and the third a swirling vortex. Each portal is guarded by a senior Librarian, and failure to provide the correct authorisation at any point means certain death.

THE VAULT OF LABYRINTHS

In one corner of the Sanctum Sanctorum lies a stasis vault, a time-sealed prison from which there can be no escape. Within the vault lie scores upon scores of tesseract labyrinths, fist-sized cubes of an alien design that are capable of imprisoning beings of pure energy, amongst whose ranks Daemons can be counted. For a Daemon, to be trapped in such a prison is literally a fate worse than death. At least when slain the Daemon's essence can return to the tides of the warp and there petition its dark master to grant it a new body. Within the chambers of a tesseract labyrinth though, the Daemon is forever isolated from the warp. As time passes, its energies decoalesce until all sense of identity is lost, and regained only if it is released – as occasionally happens when an Inquisitor of the Ordo Malleus wishes to interrogate such a creature.

Over the millennia, the Grey Knights have succeeded in sealing a few dozen Daemons within the chambers of tesseract labyrinths, thus weakening the daemonic threat by a minuscule degree. To capture a Daemon in this fashion is not easy, for the Grey Knight must not merely defeat the Daemon, but also prevent it from abandoning its mortal form when it becomes aware of the exact nature of its predicament. As yet, the Daemons captured in this fashion have almost exclusively been lesser creatures – the technique has been proven only once on one of the infinitely more powerful Greater Daemons – though the hope remains that the tesseract labyrinth might yet serve as a lasting means of victory against the daemonic.

As things stand, the Grey Knights have yet to fully trust the technological solutions offered by the tesseract labyrinths – theirs is a calling weighted in sorcery, rather than science. It is doubtful that any battle-brother truly understands the sciences behind the tesseract labyrinth. Arcane ritual has long replaced simple activation, to the point where the chants, sigils and pentagrams used to 'awaken' the tesseract labyrinth now hold far more significance in the user's mind than the series of keys that need to be pressed to engage the device's zero-point reactor. It is unsurprising then, that the Chapter's Techmarines have been unable to duplicate the technology involved, and as the Grey Knights' relations with the mysterious creator race have deteriorated to the point of hostility, it is likely these few labyrinths are the only ones the Grey Knights will ever have.

THE WARP NEXUS

The Warp Nexus lies at the very heart of the fortress monastery. In this star-shaped chamber, the very air throbs with shackled power. Fuelled by the ceaseless chants and prayers of two hundred Chapter serfs, it was the mandalas and pentagramic sigils of the Warp Nexus that maintained Titan and the Chapter Fortress amongst the turbulent tides of the immaterium.

In the millennia since, much effort has gone into maintaining the Warp Nexus. In part, this is simply because it is one of the few tangible artefacts left behind by Malcador the Sigillite. This is underpinned by the more practical goal of attempting to realign the Warp Nexus' power once again, ensuring Titan has a refuge should it be required. Thus have the cloisters of the Warp Nexus come to echo once more with canticle and intonation. Alas, no living Grey Knight has the Sigillite's knowledge of the sorceries involved, so Titan has yet to slip its worldly mooring, but rather has one foot in both worlds at any moment.

DEIMOS – THE STEEL FORGE

Upon the Grey Knights' inception, it was recognised that they, above all Space Marine Chapters, would call most frequently upon the skills of the Adeptus Mechanicus to provide them with weapons of war. To meet these needs, the Grey Knights long ago inherited their own forge world – the moon Deimos, relocated from its Martian orbit to one around Titan by the most hidden and arcane of the Adeptus Mechanicus' technologies.

Now the smog-wreathed manufactorums of Deimos thunder night and day, providing the Grey Knights with ammunition for psycannons, armour plating for Land Raiders and heavy ordnance for starships. Many of the Grey Knights' unique weapons and wargear are also produced in Deimos' subterranean halls, though certain items – chiefly Nemesis force weapons – are carefully crafted by the Chapter's Techmarines in the inviolable heart of their fortress monastery, whilst others are obtained solely under the far-reaching auspices of the Inquisition.

The handover of Deimos-forged wargear is a peculiar process, normally carried out by glassy-eyed Servitors whose senses are dulled beforehand and whose minds are scrubbed at the completion of the transaction. This is necessitated by the fact that the Grey Knights wish to preserve the secrets of Titan from the Adeptus Mechanicus, and the Adepts of Mars dare not risk exposure of their own mysteries to the Grey Knights. Such an attitude is only reasonable when you consider that both parties are guardians of perilous information which, if misused, could bring the Imperium to its knees.

BROADSWORD STATION

Broadsword Station sits in a geostationary orbit directly above Titan's fortress monastery. It is a sprawling spiderwork lattice of adamantium and ceramite, bristling with defence lasers, shield generators and torpedo batteries. Should the unthinkable happen and Titan come under direct attack, Broadsword Station would constitute the first line of defence. However, its chief purpose is to serve as the dockyard and transport hub for the Grey Knights' fleet of warships.

The Chapter's fleet would be the envy of the wider Imperium, were knowledge of its capabilities known beyond Titan. Its vessels are the fastest the Adeptus Mechanicus can provide and are commanded only by the most trusted captains and the finest Navigators of the Navis Nobilite. This purely mechanical power is further augmented by sorcerous enchantment. Charms of pathfinding enhance the Navigators' ability to steer a true course through the whirling eddies of the warp, whilst sigils of quickening accelerate the ships to otherwise unthinkable speeds. Such sorcery is volatile at best, and takes a heavy toll on the machine spirits and engines of the vessels in question.

It is therefore not uncommon for a Grey Knights starship to spend as much time being repaired, re-blessed and re-consecrated as it spends on active service. This is a steep price, but one willingly paid, for such is the speed of their ships that the Grey Knights are often the first strike force to arrive at the site of a daemonic incursion. There are many recorded instances where subsequent Imperial forces have arrived to such war zones to find the foe already defeated, with no clue as to how.

THE BANISHMENT OF DAEMONS

Chief amongst the Grey Knights' strategies concerning the vanquishing of a Daemon is the knowing of the beast's true name. Such knowledge grants great power, which is why Daemons adopt misleading pseudonyms and titles. In the hands of a learned mystic, a true name can be invoked to bind, or even banish, the Daemon in question. Ordinarily, to do so takes weeks or even months of careful preparation and ritual, lest the invoker become corrupted by the power he attempts to bind.

For a Grey Knight, however, a true name is a weapon as reliable as his storm bolter. Even the lowliest Grey Knight can invoke a true name at a moment's notice, disorienting and weakening his foe, and leaving the beast open for a killing strike from a Nemesis blade. Some in the Chapter can recall a true name to slay the Daemon's physical form, or even cast it back into the warp. To banish a Daemon in this manner is the closest that the Grey Knights can come to a lasting victory – a Daemon bodily slain will return to the mortal realm far sooner than one banished body and soul.

Alas, if true names are a Grey Knight's surest weapon against a Daemon, they are also the hardest of all to acquire. A true name is borne of the warp, and in the minds of mortal men is shifting and mutable. So it is that in the candlelit chambers of the Grey Knights' Augurium, a veritable army of ebon-cowled scribes toil in shadow, endlessly sifting through the visions reported by the Chapter's Prognosticars, searching for clues to the ever-changing true names. No scribe can be trusted with more than a fragment of a true name, lest he become corrupted by the power it contains. Thus, each scintilla of lore is inscribed onto a blessed scroll in sigils of the scribe's own blood – mere ink cannot cage such knowledge. Each is then presented for collation and interpretation by one of the Chapter's Senior Librarians and, in turn, bound into one of the blessed grimoires within the Sanctum Sanctorum.

CHAPTER ORGANISATION

The Grey Knights are unlike any other Space Marine Chapter, built around the tenets laid down by Malcador the Sigillite and the first Grand Masters. They do not follow the Codex Astartes; their organisation, ranks and deployment are dictated not by the teaching of Roboute Guilliman but by the unique demands of their war against the Dark Gods.

THE BROTHERHOODS

The bulk of the Grey Knights Chapter is organised into brotherhoods, fighting formations roughly equivalent to the Battle Companies of other Chapters. On paper, each of the Chapter's eight brotherhoods contains roughly one hundred battle-brothers under arms. This nominal figure does not include the brotherhood's officers: the Brother-Captain in active command, the Brotherhood Champion and the Grand Master who holds final responsibility over the brotherhood.

As with other Space Marine Chapters, Grey Knights are primarily organised into squads of ten battle-brothers, each of which can then further divide into two combat squads of five should the mission dictate. A Grey Knight squad is considered to remain effective with only five of its members battle-worthy, so with a small amount of duty reassignment and doctrinal flexibility, a Brother-Captain can keep his brotherhood at an acceptable fighting strength, even with a third of his warriors out of commission.

Decisions concerning the exact breakdown of squad type within a brotherhood rest entirely with its Brother-Captain and Grand Master. However, it has long been proven that a rough balance of squads – between three and seven operational units each of Terminator, Purgation and Strike Squads – is by far the most effective combination. Accordingly, all but the most maverick of commanders follow this example, and make only minor changes to suit their tactical preferences. A Grand Master often also sees fit to despatch specialists such as Chaplains, Apothecaries, Techmarines and Librarians to fight alongside a strike force.

Regardless of role, all Grey Knights squads draw their equipment from the same armoury of Nemesis force weapons, grenades, storm bolters and psi-enhanced heavy weapons. Each of a brotherhood's squads is led by a Justicar – a Grey Knight who holds a rank equivalent to sergeant. In addition to his bonds of leadership, it is the Justicar's duty to hone and focus the psychic powers of the battle-brothers he leads, and often to act as the conduit for their sorceries.

PURIFIERS AND PALADINS

In addition to the brotherhoods, the Grey Knights maintain two other main fighting bodies: the Purifiers and the Paladins. Purifiers are anathema to warp-spawn – tainted creatures wither at their touch. The Purifiers can be considered a separate and entirely unique brotherhood, albeit a small one. There are rarely more than forty Purifiers at any one time, and on those occasions when their numbers do swell, it inevitably foreshadows some great incursion.

Just as the Purifiers are exemplars of the Chapter's spiritual heart, the Paladins are its martial champions. Though they act primarily as bodyguards to the Grey Knights' Grand Masters, Paladin Squads are commonly assigned to fight alongside the brotherhoods – their skill and experience can swing the odds of even the most desperate battle.

CHAPTER COMMAND

The Grey Knights are governed and directed by a Chapter Council. At this oaken table sit eight Grand Masters and the Chapter Lord – commonly referred to as the Supreme Grand Master. Such is one of the Grey Knights' oldest traditions, as laid down at the founding by Malcador and his eight recruits. Although the Chapter Lord's rule is absolute, he can only be appointed by the unanimous consent of the Grand Masters, so it is nigh impossible for a reckless or unsuitable candidate to achieve dominion over the Chapter.

Each Grand Master holds sway over one of the Chapter's secondary bodies, such as the fleet or the armoury. However, such roles are largely honorary – the organisations in question need little oversight. A Grand Master's chief responsibility is on the battlefield. The Grey Knights are spread thin throughout the galaxy, and it is not possible for a Brother-Captain to command every strike force. Thus do the Grand Masters take charge of those most crucial of campaigns where even an experienced Brother-Captain is not thought equal to the task. This most commonly happens when one of the Conclave Diabolus – the hundred and one Greater Daemons in which the Grey Knights take special interest – is sighted in the mortal realm.

TITAN

Titan is a freezing fortress world that has sheltered the Grey Knights Chapter since its creation millennia ago. Partially terraformed centuries ago, it barely supports life, but is more than sufficient for the needs of the Grey Knights. From here the Chapter strikes out across the galaxy in their sleek silver Strike Cruisers wherever the minions of the Dark Gods arise.

Deimos
(The Steel Forge)

Broadsword Station
(Grey Knights Fleet)

AA666
Orb. Dist. 9.01AU
1.6G/Temp: 94 K
Inquisition Chamber Militant
Titthe Grade: Adeptus Non
Aestimare: A3
Population: Grey Knights Fortress
Monastery located on Titan

Strategic disposition of the Grey Knights Chapter, recorded following the return of the Planet of the Sorcerers

HALL OF CHAMPIONS

Brother-Captain Govannon Bors, High Paladin

Paladin Ancient, 98 Paladins
6 Chaplains, 12 Venerable Dreadnoughts

CHAPTER COMMAND

Lord Kaldor Draigo, Supreme Grand Master

CHAMBERS OF PURITY

Castellan Garran Crowe
44 Purifiers

1ST BROTHERHOOD

'The Swordbearers'

Grand Master Vardan Kai,
Steward of the Armoury

23 Techmarines,
75 Tech Servitors,
20 Land Raiders (including variants),
24 Rhinos, 21 Stormraven Gunships,
16 Stormtalon Gunships,
12 Stormhawk Interceptors
18 Nemesis Dreadknights

Brother-Captain Cadrig Pelenas,
1 Brotherhood Champion,
1 Brotherhood Ancient,
3 Terminator Squads,
2 Purgation Squads,
2 Interceptor Squads,
3 Strike Squads,
3 Dreadnoughts

2ND BROTHERHOOD

'The Blades of Victory'

Grand Master Vorth Mordrak,
Admiral of the Fleet

4 Battle Barges (*Fire of Dawn, Bright Sword, Emperor's Will, Redeemer of Souls*),
12 Strike Cruisers,
8 Rapid Strike Vessels,
8 Thunderhawk Gunships

Brother-Captain Arno Trevan,
1 Brotherhood Champion,
1 Brotherhood Ancient,
2 Terminator Squads,
3 Interceptor Squads,
2 Purgation Squads,
3 Strike Squads,
2 Dreadnoughts

3RD BROTHERHOOD

'The Wardmakers'

Grand Master Aldrik Voldus,
Warden of the Librarius

3 Epistolaries,
12 Codiciers,
9 Lexicanum,
12 Acolytum

Brother-Captain Arvann Stern,
1 Brotherhood Champion,
1 Brotherhood Ancient,
3 Terminator Squads,
2 Interceptor Squads,
3 Purgation Squads,
2 Strike Squads,
3 Dreadnoughts

4TH BROTHERHOOD

'The Prescient Brethren'

Grand Master Drystann Cromm,
Keeper of the Augurium

12 Prognosticars,
50 Mono-task Servitors

Brother-Captain Ionan Grud,
1 Brotherhood Champion,
2 Terminator Squads,
3 Interceptor Squads,
2 Purgation Squads,
3 Strike Squads,
3 Dreadnoughts

5TH BROTHERHOOD

'The Preservers'

Grand Master Rothwyr Morvans,
Protector of the Sanctum Sanctorum

12 Apothecaries

Brother-Captain Tauros Hendron,
1 Brotherhood Champion,
2 Terminator Squads,
2 Interceptor Squads,
2 Purgation Squads,
4 Strike Squads,
5 Dreadnoughts

6TH BROTHERHOOD

'The Rapiers'

Grand Master Anval Laraon,
High Seneschal of the Fortress

271 Chapter Equerries,
500 Servitors

Brother-Captain Caddon Varn,
1 Brotherhood Champion,
2 Terminator Squads,
3 Interceptor Squads,
2 Purgation Squads,
3 Strike Squads,
2 Dreadnoughts

7TH BROTHERHOOD

'The Exactors'

Grand Master Covan Leorac,
Representative to the Inquisition

24 Scribes, 3 Astropaths

Brother-Captain Darig Tegvar,
1 Brotherhood Champion,
3 Terminator Squads,
2 Interceptor Squads,
3 Purgation Squads,
2 Strike Squads,
2 Dreadnoughts

8TH BROTHERHOOD

'The Silver Blades'

Grand Master Aidan Perdron,
Knight Commander of the Recruits

32 Neophytes,
1,005 Recruits,
38 Mono-task Servitors

Brother-Captain Mithrac Tor,
1 Brotherhood Champion,
3 Terminator Squads,
2 Interceptor Squads,
3 Purgation Squads,
2 Strike Squads,
1 Dreadnought

THE BROTHERHOODS

1st Brotherhood 'The Swordbearers'

The Grand Master of the 1st holds the title of Steward of the Armoury, and the brotherhood maintains and administers the Chapter's reserves of Land Raiders, Stormhawk Interceptors, and Stormtalon and Stormraven Gunships. As such, the Swordbearers are often called upon when the Grey Knights require armoured or aerial support, and in their ranks are many of the finest pilots of the Chapter. The Grand Master oversees these sacred war machines and the Techmarines that maintain them, ensuring that they remain in perfect fighting condition. The battle-brothers of the Swordbearers are drilled to fight in perfect unison with these hallowed war machines, shattering the ranks of the enemy to allow barrages of stormstrike missiles and godhammer lascannon fire to blast apart towering Greater Daemons as they come lumbering through warp rifts.

2nd Brotherhood 'The Blades of Victory'

The Blades of Victory have a well-deserved reputation for rapid deployment and swift strikes, even by the standards of the Grey Knights. The brotherhood makes use of large numbers of Interceptor and Strike Squads, using mass teleportation tactics to outmanoeuvre their enemies. The 2nd is often in the vanguard of combined brotherhood assaults, bursting onto the battlefield to form a beachhead and seeding the way for heavier troops to follow. As Admiral of the Fleet, the Grand Master of the 2nd excels at the art of military manoeuvres and deployment, ensuring the Grey Knights' rapid deployment to the war zone. With the predictions of the Prognosticars providing vital tactical information, the Grey Knights fleet is often able to deliver strike forces to the battlefield before the foe has even made its arrival.

3rd Brotherhood 'The Wardmakers'

The Wardmakers have always held a place of honour within the Chapter. It was, according to legend, Janus' own brotherhood, and throughout the long history of the Grey Knights it has fostered many of the Chapter's greatest heroes. Kaldor Draigo was Brother-Captain and then Grand Master of the 3rd, and Arvann Stern serves as the current Brother-Captain. The Wardmakers, led by the Warden of the Librarius, have authority over the Librarium Daemonica, and their Librarians are charged with drilling new recruits in the practice of psychic incantation. A Grey Knights Librarian is a psyker of prodigious might, even among his gifted brethren, capable of unleashing warp energies on the battlefield to devastating effect, even tearing realspace open to cast Daemons back into the warp before sealing the rift once more.

4th Brotherhood 'The Prescient Brethren'

The Keeper of the Augurium commands the 4th, and within the ranks of this brotherhood are many of the Chapter's most potent psykers, warriors with an instinctual understanding of the warp that goes beyond even that of their peers. It is from the Prescient Brethren that new Prognosticars are often chosen, after they are too badly wounded to fight, or if they have shown particular aptitude and are considered too valuable an asset to risk on the battlefield. Members of the Prescient Brethren often have the ability to sense danger before it materialises, and they use this to stalk their enemy relentlessly and to devise highly effective ambushes in which to snare their foe. The ability to anticipate their enemies' manoeuvres also enhances their martial abilities, and some of the greatest duellists in the Chapter's history have come from the Prescient Brethren.

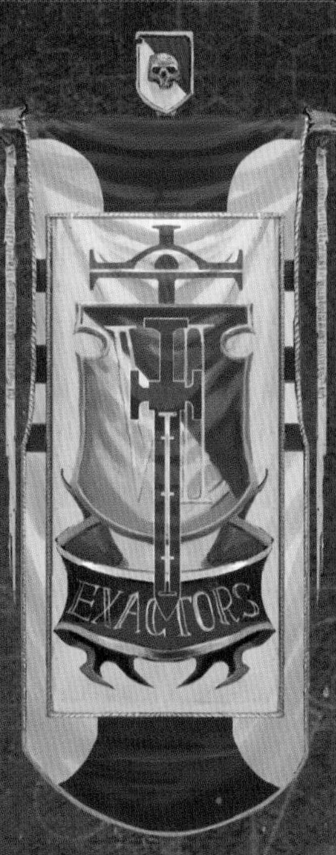

5th Brotherhood 'The Preservers'

The responsibility of the Chapter's greatest legacy, its gene-seed, lies with the 5th, for it is in this brotherhood that Apothecaries are trained in their vital duties. The Preservers are also wardens of the Grey Knights' Dreadnoughts, in which battle-brothers too injured to be healed can continue to serve. To be Grand Master of the 5th and Protector of the Sanctum Sanctorum requires great humility, for many of the Dreadnoughts they command house battle-brothers with experience dating back millennia. Fallen warriors newly entombed inside Dreadnoughts also fight with the 5th, learning through combat how to wield the raw power of their machine spirit. Where the Preservers battle, the ground shakes beneath pounding iron feet as the fury of these deathless war machines is brutally released upon whatever dares stand before them.

6th Brotherhood 'The Rapiers'

Those who serve as High Seneschal of the Fortress are stringent taskmasters, their dedication to excellency and efficiency reflected in the warriors of their brotherhood. The Grey Knights cannot tolerate wasted effort or manpower, and in the Council of Grand Masters it is often the High Seneschal who is tasked with crafting the most elite and deadly strike forces.

The Rapiers understand that a strategically deployed, purpose-built strike force can inflict as much damage as an entire army. Rather than using destructive artillery batteries and orbital bombardments, the 6th rely on surgical strikes, trusting the training and expertise of small squads of specialists to get the job done. Where bulk of numbers is necessary, the High Seneschal deploys mindless Servitors to bog down the enemy, allowing his Grey Knights to focus on high-risk targets.

7th Brotherhood 'The Exactors'

The Inquisition and the Grey Knights were founded at the same time during the darkest days of the Horus Heresy and, though created to act independently of one another, their goals continue to align.

The Exactors have a long history of operating alongside the Ordo Malleus, and as a result respected Inquisitors are often able to call upon them for aid. In return, the Exactors rely on the Inquisition to provide watchful eyes throughout the Imperium, and to supply them with auxiliary forces whenever and wherever they are needed. The 7th often fight alongside Imperial troops requisitioned by the Inquisition, utilising platoons of Astra Militarum soldiers to hold key battlefield positions or Inquisitorial Acolytes to quell daemonic uprisings. Those brave troops who survive their missions with the Exactors continue to serve the Chapter indefinitely as mind-scoured Servitors.

8th Brotherhood 'The Silver Blades'

When a newly forged battle-brother joins the ranks of the Grey Knights he will typically be sequestered to the 8th Brotherhood. He may then find a place within one of the other brotherhoods, depending on his natural talents and the favour of the Grand Masters, or he may choose to remain with the Silver Blades. Those who remain dedicate themselves to continual training, running the trials of initiation again and again in the pursuit of martial perfection. Led by the Knight Commander, the warriors of the 8th fight in fluid configurations, changing tactics swiftly during combat and between engagements. Any available weapon is put to use, and no strategy or manoeuvre is preferred over any other. A Silver Sword aims to be proficient in the use of every armament, and to know the strength in every strike force and the weakness in every enemy.

HERALDRY OF TITAN

The Grey Knights have endured for millennia, their Chapter built upon a web of ancient traditions and oaths. These sacred customs and doctrines are reflected in the weapons they use, the armour they wear and the heraldry they bear, each one a part of their proud history.

CRUSADER HELM

Grey Knights use older patterns of helmets – known as Crusader helms – for both their power and Terminator armour, giving their squads a distinctive appearance when placed alongside other Adeptus Astartes.

STORM BOLTER

Grey Knight Terminator armour incorporates a wrist-mounted storm bolter, an ancient pattern that allows them to wield their halberd unimpeded.

OATH SHIELD

Battle-brothers display their heraldry upon their shields, the simple designs displaying their deeds and glories. As a Grey Knight advances in rank he will add to his shield to reflect his elevated standing within the Chapter.

NEMESIS FORCE HALBERD

Every Grey Knight Terminator carries a force blade attuned to his psychic will. The ritual of dedication binds the weapon to its bearer, and it falls to the battle-brother to preserve and honour his weapon in combat. After years of battle a Grey Knight's force weapon will retain a piece of his psyche imprinted upon its blade that will live on long after he has fallen in combat.

PURITY SEALS

When a Grey Knights battle-brother dons his armour its seals are blessed in complex and ancient rituals to preserve their integrity and keep the warrior safe from attacks both mundane and mystical. When a battle-brother returns to Titan it is a measure of his skill in battle and strength of will should these seals remain unbroken.

ARMOUR ETCHINGS

Each Grey Knight's armour is an ancient relic drawn from the Chapter's armouries and has often been worn by many warriors before him. Sometimes their names or deeds will be etched upon the plates and edges of their armour, a preserved memory of their glory.

Radomen Kyr
Sword of Dusk

Atrophius Axen
Drakesbane

Yullus Foric
The Penitent Lord

Tarvus Solonius
Castellan Primus

Ulleceus Barron
The Purifying Light

Velonn Hartus
The August Blade

Phalocles Leoben
Thrice-risen

Vul Druchna
The Twilight Flame

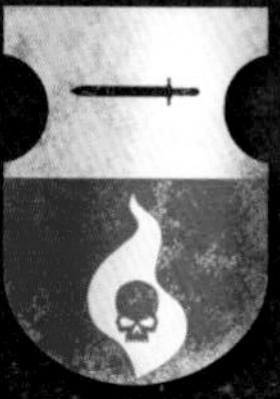

Krassus Valnar
Purifier of Aosa

Osryck Valderon
Silverbrand

Colodus Thorne
Saviour of Hyperosa

Iryan Farros
The Redeemed

Keldan Clyffe
Torchbearer

Tanarion Gour
The Foereaper

Arvann Stern
Bane of M'kachen

Galdiman Hadris
of the Twelve Pyres

Kyel Adronus
Malleus Infernalus

Eldrius Tremayne
Bringer of Silence

Vendt Malornus
Magister of Swords

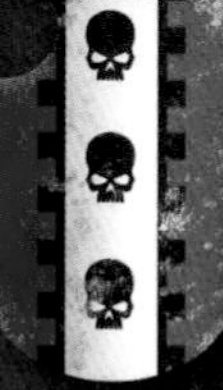

Ghardren Voctus
The Clenched Fist

Mordat Dhask
Hand of Judgemen

Admar Scythus
Bane of
the Faithless

Uriah Tayne
Slayer of the
Bright King

Ignatius Trau
The Hammer
of Reason

Arvall Dyrus
Knight of the
Silver Path

Wilthar Hluss
The Emancipator
of Trilox

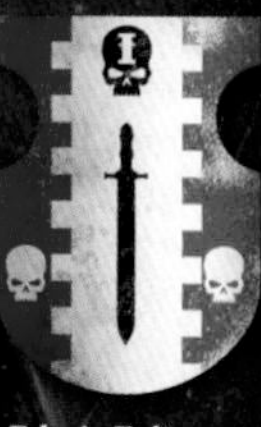

Ederic Foltane
Master of the
Formosean Rites

Hardrim Hahl
Scribe of the
12th Canticle

Red, white and black are the common colours of almost all Grey Knights heraldry, these being colours used by the first Grand Masters when they forsook their Legions and embraced the sacred duty the Emperor had given them. Every battle-brother's heraldry is unique, and changes over long centuries of service to reflect their greatest deeds. For many of the Grey Knights, this is the only record of their actions throughout the entire Imperium.

Each icon and colour has its own esoteric meaning within the Chapter; skulls indicate the quelling of powerful daemonic foes and swords battlefield honours, for example. Crenellated lines, divisions of colour and which colour is ascendant all represent a battle-brother's position within his brotherhood, the colour, direction and gradient of the line or division each having its own meaning. To outsiders, the differences are often too subtle to notice, but they speak volumes within the Chapter.

Grey Knights will occasionally incorporate symbology of their allies into their heraldry, if they are especially deserving. A skull may bear the icon of the Inquisition, showing a great victory won over a potent daemonic foe with the aid of one of the Holy Ordos. Sometimes a battle-brother will take the icon of an ally which has been eradicated in battle, the only memento of their existence captured upon the battle-brother's shield, a forlorn reminder of their service to the Grey Knights while they lived. However, it is rare for symbols to be adopted in this way as there are few allies worthy enough to earn the respect of the Grey Knights.

The icon of a sword is a powerful symbol, representing an act that preserved the battle-brother's squad, turned the tide of an important confrontation or brought about the destruction of a most hated foe. A white sword on red is a symbol of the Emperor's mercy, an act considered inspired by the Master of Mankind's benevolence. A black sword on red is a measure of the Emperor's wrath and is granted for acts of vengeance. Rarer are rec swords on black that show the Emperor's righteous rage, and the madness that faith can bring. A battle-brother that bears a rec sword has been driven to the edge of his duty and managed to claw his way back.

The stylized symbol of the Imperial Aquila is a sacred icon to the Grey Knights, and only its most proven heroes bear it upon their heraldry. It represents a great deed of service to the Emperor, something so significant as to eclipse all other glories. Typically only Grand Masters, Brother-Captains and Paladins will be seen wearing the Aquila dominate, but in rare cases a Justicar or distinguished battle-brother will bear the symbol. The nature of this decoration is as varied as the battle-brothers honoured by it, but all indicate unfailing devotion to the Emperor.

TAPESTRY OF CHAOS

Item 258-3C-6: Chart of known warp storms – produced by the Admiral of the Fleet for the Sanctum Sanctorum.

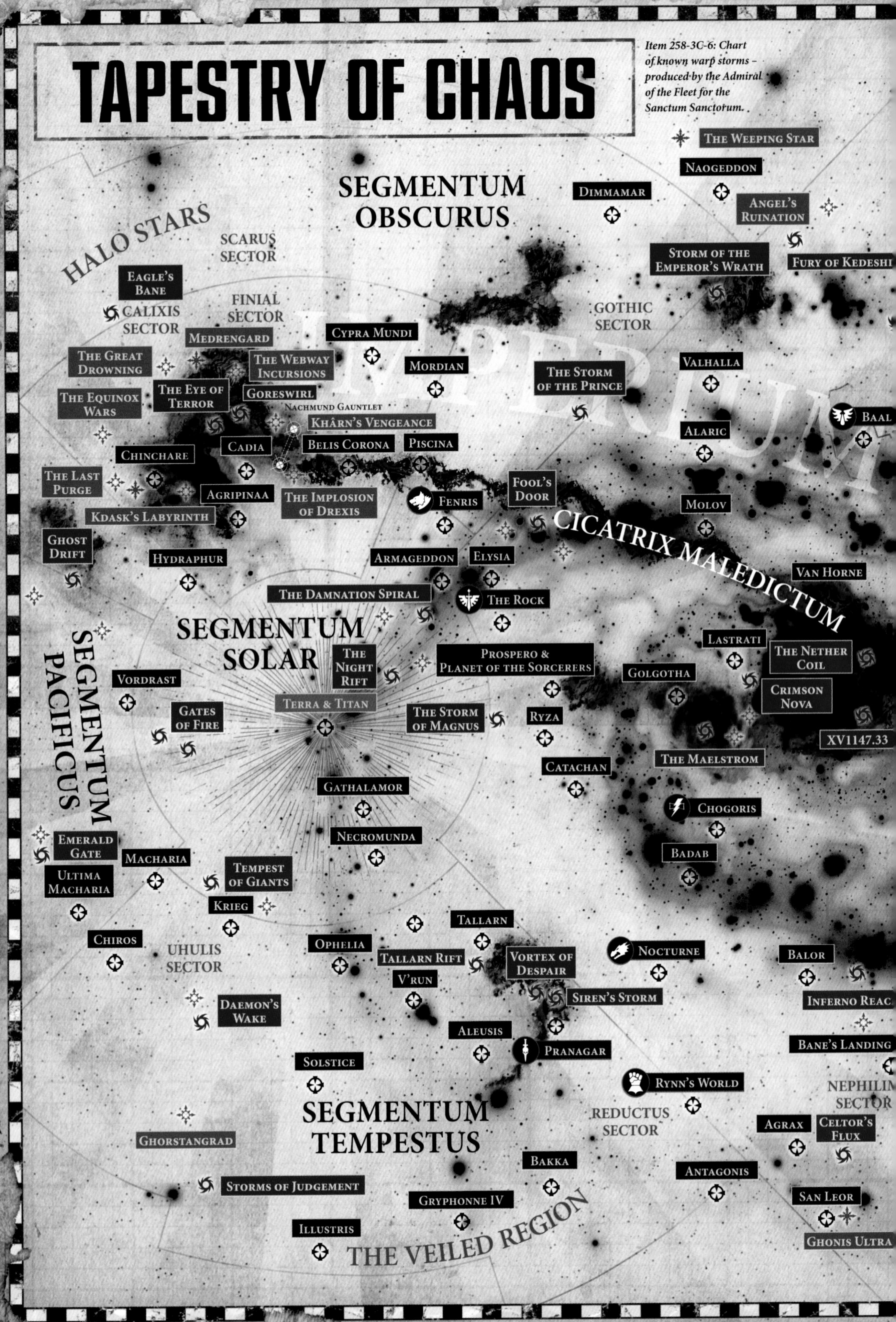

The Weeping Star
Naogeddon
Dimmamar
Angel's Ruination
Segmentum Obscurus
Halo Stars
Scarus Sector
Storm of the Emperor's Wrath
Fury of Kedeshi
Eagle's Bane
Calixis Sector
Finial Sector
Gothic Sector
Imperium
Medrengard
Cypra Mundi
The Great Drowning
The Webway Incursions
Mordian
The Storm of the Prince
Valhalla
The Equinox Wars
The Eye of Terror
Goreswirl
Nachmund Gauntlet
Khârn's Vengeance
Baal
Alaric
Chinchare
Cadia
Belis Corona
Piscina
The Last Purge
Agripinaa
The Implosion of Drexis
Fenris
Fool's Door
Molov
Kdask's Labyrinth
Cicatrix Maledictum
Ghost Drift
Hydraphur
Armageddon
Elysia
Van Horne
The Damnation Spiral
The Rock
Segmentum Solar
Segmentum Pacificus
The Night Rift
Prospero & Planet of the Sorcerers
Lastrati
The Nether Coil
Golgotha
Crimson Nova
Vordrast
Terra & Titan
Gates of Fire
The Storm of Magnus
Ryza
XV1147.33
The Maelstrom
Catachan
Gathalamor
Chogoris
Emerald Gate
Necromunda
Badab
Macharia
Tempest of Giants
Ultima Macharia
Krieg
Tallarn
Chiros
Uhulis Sector
Ophelia
Tallarn Rift
Vortex of Despair
Nocturne
Balor
V'run
Siren's Storm
Inferno Reac
Daemon's Wake
Aleusis
Pranagar
Bane's Landing
Solstice
Rynn's World
Nephilim Sector
Segmentum Tempestus
Reductus Sector
Agrax
Celtor's Flux
Ghorstangrad
Bakka
Antagonis
Storms of Judgement
San Leor
Gryphonne IV
Illustris
The Veiled Region
Ghonis Ultra

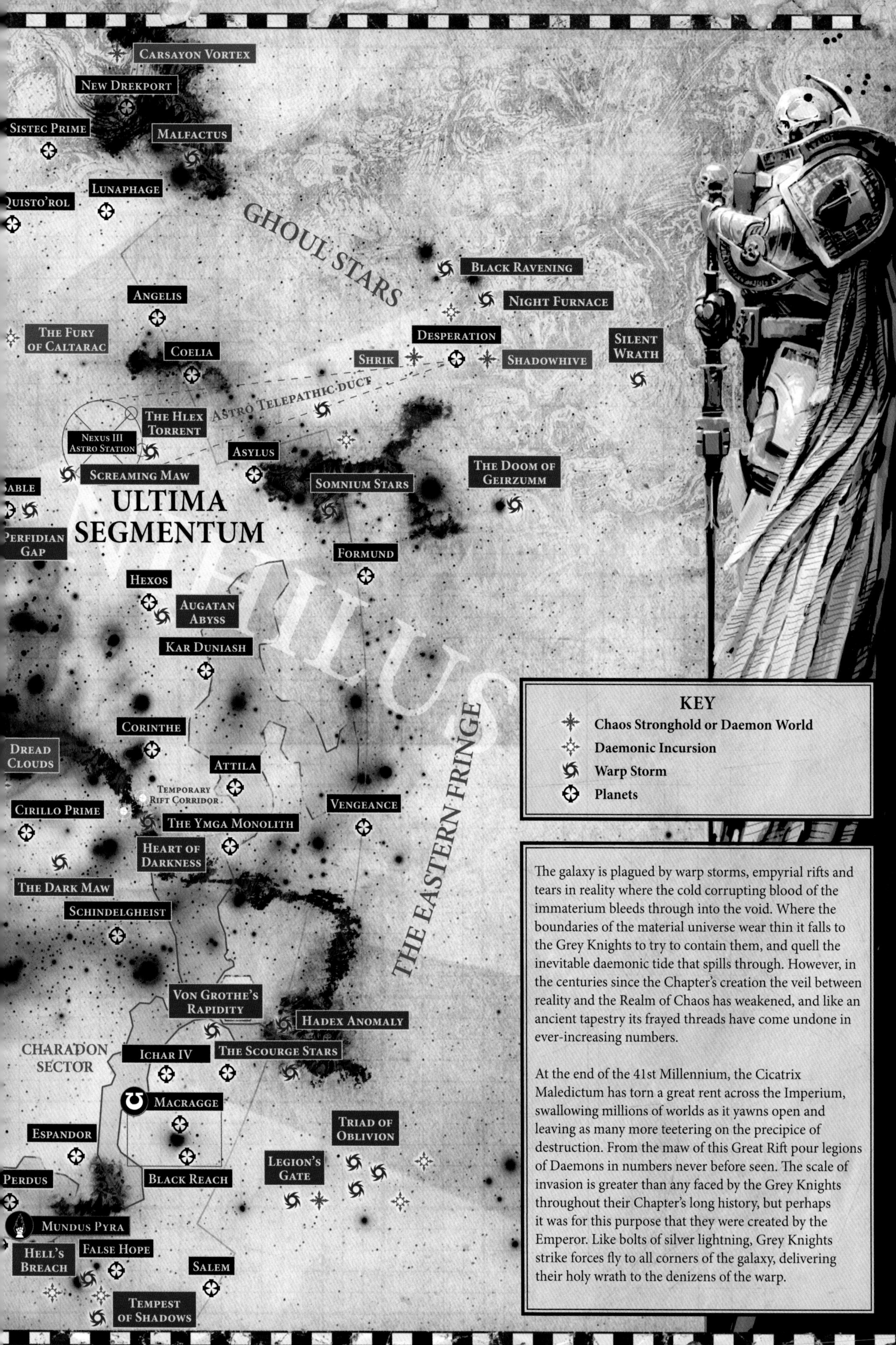

The galaxy is plagued by warp storms, empyrial rifts and tears in reality where the cold corrupting blood of the immaterium bleeds through into the void. Where the boundaries of the material universe wear thin it falls to the Grey Knights to try to contain them, and quell the inevitable daemonic tide that spills through. However, in the centuries since the Chapter's creation the veil between reality and the Realm of Chaos has weakened, and like an ancient tapestry its frayed threads have come undone in ever-increasing numbers.

At the end of the 41st Millennium, the Cicatrix Maledictum has torn a great rent across the Imperium, swallowing millions of worlds as it yawns open and leaving as many more teetering on the precipice of destruction. From the maw of this Great Rift pour legions of Daemons in numbers never before seen. The scale of invasion is greater than any faced by the Grey Knights throughout their Chapter's long history, but perhaps it was for this purpose that they were created by the Emperor. Like bolts of silver lightning, Grey Knights strike forces fly to all corners of the galaxy, delivering their holy wrath to the denizens of the warp.

They are the Emperor's final boon to Mankind, an army of unfaltering and incorruptible warriors born of forgotten science. They are the Grey Knights – the only true defence against the Daemons of Chaos.

DEEDS OF LEGEND

The Grey Knights have fought to hold back the daemonic hordes of the Dark Gods for a hundred centuries, waging their war in secret against an unrelenting and tireless foe. Their deeds are known outside the Chapter only as myths and legends, tales of silver-armoured warriors saving Humanity from the beasts of nightmare.

M31–M34 AGE OF WARDING

The 666th Chapter

Titan returns to the galaxy during the Second Founding, and the Inquisition records the Grey Knights as the 666th Chapter. Under a veil of secrecy the Chapter begins its work, hunting down the daemonic enemies that threaten the Imperium.

Fate Unravels

The Daemon Ix'thar'ganix, the Slayer of Destinies, foresees the role that the Grey Knights will play in his downfall, and the threat they may eventually pose to the Dark Gods. Overcome with his own cunning the Lord of Change begins a plan that will take eight thousand years to come to fruition, seeding lesser Daemons on worlds all across the Imperium so that he might subtly manipulate future events.

The Ghost Quell

On the desolate planet of Forlor, the Grey Knights corner the radical Inquisitor Vetrix. After enacting the Psycantic Necrolarus upon the Segmentum Solar, Vetrix has been declared a heretic by his Ordo. The Inquisitor is dragged back to the dungeons of Titan, pleading with his stony-faced captors that the Necrolarus is the Imperium's only hope for survival.

The Final Sanction

Neodan, Brother-Captain of the 5th Brotherhood, slays the Butcher of Xor, an abattoir overseer possessed by a Daemon of Khorne. Only after the Daemon and its servants have been dealt with does Neodan discover that the creature had been tainting the meat-beasts of the blood factorums, and spreading them across Xor and its neighbouring worlds. With no knowledge of how far the corrupted flesh has spread, Neodan declares a final sanction against Xor, condemning millions to death rather than risking a daemonic incursion.

The Hollow Cult

During their long war against the Hollow Cult and its many-limbed pleasure god, the Grey Knights lose almost the entire 7th Brotherhood. The cult lays a series of cunning ambushes for the Grey Knights, bending reality to isolate each of the battle-brothers and overwhelm them in a tide of daemonic flesh. The Grey Knights' retribution is absolute, and Supreme Grand Master Calastan gathers the full might of the Chapter against the cult. In the end, the only memory of the Hollow Cult that remains is recorded in faded ink within the Sanctum Sanctorum in the Citadel of Titan.

The Lost Brotherhood

Brother-Captain Edeon leads a number of squads of the 2nd Brotherhood into the Veiled Region seeking the Daemonafex. All communication ceases, and eventually the Council of Titan declares them lost.

M35–M36 AGE OF FOREBODING

The Haunting of Titan

The Chambers of Purity are sullied by haunting spectres of the warp: the ghosts of vanquished foes clawing at the walls of reality and whispering portents of future catastrophe. The creatures warn of a time when the light of the Emperor will fail and the Grey Knights will stand alone against the darkness, the fate of Humanity resting upon the razor edges of their blades. The Purifiers endure the maddened tirades of these ghosts and the visions of the Imperium fallen into darkness and fire; they believe these shades are but echoes of the monsters they purport to be, barely connected to the warp and able to do no more than spew forth lies. The Purifiers also know, however, that the daemonic ghosts are a symptom of something ancient and powerful that slumbers beneath the surface of Titan…

Eye of the Storm

A warp storm descends on the Rorn System in the wake of the Pallid Prince and his Daemon host. A squad of Grey Knights are trapped by the storm on the Rorn Primarex shipyard, having destroyed the Pallid Prince and his warp-iron vessel. Unwilling to risk discovery by the citizens of Rorn III, and denied warp travel by the storm, the Grey Knights set out into the void at sub-light speeds, the battle-brothers entering stasis for their millennia-long voyage back to Titan.

A Brotherhood Out of Time

Nearly two thousand years after their disappearance, word reaches Titan of the lost Brother-Captain Edeon and his brothers. Unbeknownst to the Chapter, Edeon had followed the Daemonafex and its thralls into an area of warp that owed its existence to the echoes of forgotten moments. Edeon and his Grey Knights fought at the foot of the Daemon's Fortress of Deceit, each day falling to grievous wounds only to rise again, borne up by their unwavering resolve and psychic fury. Faced with their combined might, the Daemonafex was finally cast down, though it was to cost Edeon and his brothers their lives in the material realm. On their return to realspace, their bodies begin to atrophy at an alarming rate. Before he dies, the Brother-Captain only has time to send a coded signal to Titan, telling of the brotherhood's victory.

A Thousand Deaths

Xorgar the Cruel ascends to Daemonhood amid the blood-drenched battlefields of the Rusting War. The Grey Knights already fighting against the Ragged Host focus their attentions on Xorgar and slay him before he can fully manifest his newfound powers. However, it amuses the Dark Gods to torment their vassal by giving him life once more, and for the next twelve years the Grey Knights hunt and kill Xorgar hundreds of times on scores of worlds. Only when the Daemon's mortal shell is destroyed for the thousandth time do the gods tire of their game.

A Daemon Assassin

The Slaaneshi Daemon assassin Hex'tan attempts to sneak onto Titan and hide among an intake of recruits. Initially successful, the Daemon lurks on the plains of the Xanadu Regio among the bones of the dead, awaiting a suitable candidate to possess and carry it back to the citadel.

However, the creature's plans unravel when a strong-willed future Grey Knight hunts it down and imprisons it in the corpse of another recruit, unaware that this was not part of his trial.

The Quiet Heresy

Tzeentchian Daemons rob the populace of Sundel of speech, every citizen rendered mute by warp sorceries. In the silence that follows the Cult of the Severed Tongue is born, its debased members torturing and killing men and women with no voices to scream. For a year the cult reigns without opposition, turning the planet into a silent hell where corpses rot in the streets and men and women live like vermin in the shadows, fearful of making the slightest sound that will give them away. The Grey Knights confront the cult as Sundel stands on the verge of utter destruction, its cities completely given over to worshipping the very Daemons that orchestrated their ruin. In the empty silence, the only sounds to be heard are the bark of storm bolters and the crackle of Nemesis force weapons as the Grey Knights purify the planet and annihilate any in their path.

M37–M39 AGE OF EXECRATION

The Tarnished Blade

The Astral Blades Space Marine Chapter is led down the path to Chaos by their prideful Chapter Master, who has been possessed by the Daemon Etherak the Unrepentant. The Daemon's servants use sorcery to possess almost every battle-brother within the Chapter's subterranean fortress monastery one by one, slaughtering those strong enough to resist. As the blood of the last of the fallen is still cooling, the possessed Space Marines plunder the Chapter's gene-seed stores and set off for the Eye of Terror. However, when their Battle Barge, *Sword of Stars*, reaches high orbit, the Grey Knights are waiting for them. In the furious battle that ensues Grey Knight Terminators teleport onto the bridge of the Battle Barge and banish Etherak back into the warp in the midst of a furious melee. Broken in body and spirit, the Chapter Master of the Astral Blades accepts the Emperor's mercy delivered at the hands of his 'saviours'.

Daemon Maze

The Heretek, Malforea the Mad, constructs a vast maze structure of ghost-glass and etheric siphons in an attempt to harness the power of the warp for his corrupt machines. The maze has the unintentional side effect of trapping Daemons, the creatures drawn toward the device only to become lost within its multi-dimensional twists and turns. When the Daemon Prince Kaslidi becomes ensnared, its rage shakes the structure to its foundations and it becomes a locus for the creature's essence. The Grey Knights arrive to find the Heretek a puppet of Kaslidi and his world on the verge of a full-blown daemonic incursion. To defeat the Daemon Prince, the Grey Knights enter the maze, hunting down the Daemons trapped within. A battle of reflections and illusions ensues, the battle-brothers surrounded by flickering daemonic faces and psychic manifestations. Reaching the centre of the maze the Grey Knight Justicar cuts down the Malforea flesh-puppet and shatters the ghost-glass face of Kaslidi, bringing down the structure and casting the Daemons back into the warp.

M40–M41 AGE OF ANATHEMA

The Damned Voyage

The Grey Knights Strike Cruiser *Titan's Hand* suffers a catastrophic Geller field failure, leaving the ship unshielded against the warp. Almost at once, the *Hand* is engulfed with daemonic creatures hungry for the souls of those on board. The Grey Knights stand haloed by psychic energy, each one shielding his mind and body with the blessed seals of the Aegis. Against servitors and Chapter serfs turned into puppets of Chaos, the battle-brothers fight to reclaim their vessel. When the *Hand* finally makes an emergency translation back into realspace the surviving Grey Knights stand in the midst of a command bridge covered in the remains of their unfortunate crew.

Convocation of Souls

The public execution of 666 heretics on the planet of Horvar III has terrible consequences. Through the pageantry and extravagance of the event the nearsighted planetary governor unwittingly completes an ancient daemonic ritual. As the last heretic dies with a curse upon his lips, the circle of sorcery is complete and a gateway to the warp is opened. The Chaos well yawns wide and Daemons spill out into the mass of terrified citizens. In a matter of hours Horvar III is turned into an arena of madness and death. The unfortunate planetary governor is possessed by the Slaaneshi Daemon Prince Laesydra and the Golden Host is released upon the world.

The Grey Knights arrive in force to discover Laesydra hosting blood games with the surviving citizens, the Daemon forcing them to commit unspeakable acts of violence against each other or be hurled into the warp-well. Turning its attention to this new foe, Laesydra crafts a series of tests for the Space Marines, shaping tangled labyrinths of living, screaming flesh around them and sending Seekers of Slaanesh to hunt them down. The hunters soon become the hunted, however, and the Grey Knights fight their way to the warp-well where the Daemon Prince is holding court over the mutilated remains of Horvar's citizens, wearing the skin of their governor. At the cost of the lives of a score of Grey Knights the Daemon is cast back into the warp. Before the battle-brothers depart they pile the citizens' tortured bodies onto of the corpses of the executed heretics, sealing the warp-well with the blood of innocents.

The First Battle for Armageddon

The space hulk *Devourer of Stars* appears in the Armageddon System. Upon reaching orbit, it disgorges a vast Chaos horde – led by the infamous Daemon Primarch Angron – upon the continent Armageddon Prime. The Chaos horde initially makes great gains, taking control of Armageddon Prime and threatening to overwhelm Armageddon Secundus. However, the defences of the lower continent hold – chiefly due to the valour of Logan Grimnar and his Space Wolves – long enough for a full brotherhood of Grey Knights to arrive, carrying the battle directly to Angron himself. In a titanic clash, Angron and his Bloodthirster honour guard are eventually bested, though it costs the lives of almost the full brotherhood.

In the aftermath of the battle, the Inquisition begins a thorough programme of mindwipes and executions of those Guardsmen and hive defenders who had taken part in the war, in order to contain knowledge of both Daemons and of the Grey Knights. However, many thousands slip through the tightening noose, aided by Logan Grimnar who vehemently abhors such practices. Thus is the Inquisition given cause to pay closer attention to the Space Wolves in the years that follow.

The Cleansing of Acralem

The notorious Daemon Prince M'kar the Reborn launches an attack on the world of Acralem, seeking to claim it as a throne world from which he can carve an empire. Acting on an Inquisitional request, the Grey Knights spearhead the Imperium's counter-offensive, and in the final battle the young Kaldor Draigo makes his name by banishing the Daemon Prince.

The Battle of the Ghost Halls

A dire vision from the Prognosticars results in a Grey Knights strike force being dispatched to an empty point in space. On arrival the strike force encounters the massive, bio-acid scorched hulk of Craftworld Malan'tai. Though its inhabitants have all but been destroyed by Tyranids, Malan'tai is not so empty as it first appears. The ancient Keeper of Secrets N'kari and his kind stalk the fallen halls, growing bloated with power on Eldar spirit stones. Fortunately, the Prognosticars bade Brother-Captain Pelenas to take as many Purifiers as he could muster.

As the Grey Knights launch their assault on despoiled Malan'tai, the Purifiers lead the charge. Fire roars through the desolate halls like a hungry spirit, scattering those hellspawn that survive and leaving them ripe prey for the advancing Grey Knights. N'kari is finally cornered in the shattered Dome of Crystal Seers. The Daemon fights with fury, and savagely strikes down Pelenas. Yet, before the Daemon can land the killing blow on the fallen Brother-Captain, Justicar Thawn throws himself into the Daemon's path and is laid low in his Captain's place. With N'kari's weapon momentarily embedded in Thawn's flesh, the surviving Purifiers are able to complete the ritual of Twelve Bloody Swords, which drains N'kari of his stolen power and leaves him vulnerable to Pelenas' deathblow.

After the battle, the strike force returns to Titan with the bodies of the fallen. A score of Purifiers remains aboard the craftworld, standing guard over the empty halls.

The Raxos Civil War

Civil war comes to the hive world of Raxos when the planetary governor convinces some of the local military forces to rise up against his own regime. When the insurrectionists seize control of a Deathstrike missile battery, the resulting bombardment disrupts Raxos' tectonic stability. Millions die in the span of a few days. The governor – later revealed to be Tzeentch's Changeling in disguise – harnesses the psychic upheaval to summon hundreds of his fellow Daemons.

Alerted to the situation on Raxos, Grey Knights from four brotherhoods arrive amidst the ongoing civil war. Grand Master Drystann Cromm splits his Grey Knights into several strike forces – three to attack the portals from which the Daemons are drawing their power, and a fourth, under Brother-Captain Stern, to aid the spaceport's fleeing refugee shuttles.

Whilst Stern safeguards the spaceport, Cromm casts broken fingerbones of martyred saints at the mouth of each portal to prevent further Daemons manifesting, and then performs the rites of cleansing and exorcism that finally seal the portals and banish the remaining Daemons. Yet, as the first refugee shuttles lift off, Stern grows uneasy – the Changeling's psychic spoor still lingers.

With grim certainty, Stern realises that the Daemon must have boarded one of the refugee shuttles now heading for outer orbit. Knowing that his forces are too few to have any hope of uncovering the hidden Changeling in time, but all too aware of the anarchy that the Daemon will unleash should it reach another populated world, Stern orders the Battle Barge *Bright Sword* to destroy the shuttles. Hundreds of thousands are slain in the ensuing salvo, their lives sacrificed to preserve millions on distant worlds.

The Fall of the Red Talon

Brother-Captain Stern oversees the destruction of the Cult of the Red Talon.

The Black Planet

Garran Crowe battles Skulltaker, Daemon Champion of Khorne, on the Black Planet and, though he cannot best him in combat, he buys enough time for his brothers to foil the Daemon's plans.

The Battle of Kornovin

Supreme Grand Master Geronitan is slain at the hands of the Daemon Primarch Mortarion. Grand Master Kaldor Draigo is elevated to the rank of Supreme Grand Master amidst the din of the battlefield and vows vengeance on Mortarion. Alone and unaided, Draigo smashes his way through Mortarion's corrupted Deathshroud bodyguard and strikes the Primarch to the ground with a blow empowered by his fury at Geronitan's death. He then carves Supreme Grand Master Geronitan's name on the Daemon's vile heart. Though Mortarion ultimately escapes, it is many long years before he can enter the mortal realm once more.

The Plague of Madness

Supreme Grand Master Kaldor Draigo leads three full Grey Knights brotherhoods against Ix'thar'ganix, the Slayer of Destinies, and his unwitting Nurgle pawn, Lurgon, on the doomed world of Decimalus.

The Pandemonium of Sondheim V

The world of Sondheim V is overwhelmed by Tyranids of Hive Fleet Kraken just as M'kar the Reborn transforms the world into his own private pandemonium. The Sky Sentinels Chapter respond, but judge the world irretrievable and make preparations to begin Exterminatus. This is delayed by the arrival of a Grey Knights strike force under the command of Grand Master Vardan Kai. Kai concurs with the Sky Sentinels' assessment but orders a stay of execution whilst he and his battle-brothers attempt to capture the Book of Pandegaras – the cursed tome with whose power M'kar has mutated the planet.

Upon landing, Kai discovers the nightmarish fusion of daemonic and Tyranid infestations have transformed Sondheim V into a death world. When Kai's forces reach the temple in which the tome lies, they discover the building has been completely subsumed by a knot of Tyranid spore chimneys. Unperturbed, the Grey Knights hack their way through the twisted biomatter. Within seconds of the first blow falling, Kai's forces come under attack by waves of Hormagaunts and Gargoyles. By the time Kai finally carves a path into the lower levels of the temple, larger creatures start to arrive, and the Grey Knights' casualties begin to tell. Yet as Kai finally lays his hand upon the Book of Pandegaras, unexpected aid arrives. Just as the earlier strike on the biostructures had roused the Hive Mind's ire, so too does the violation of the evil tome now bring forth the Daemons' wrath, and the twisted ruins erupt into the anarchy of a three-way battle.

Amid the chaos, Kai makes contact with the Sky Sentinels fleet, who begin a systematic bombardment of the temple site. The Grey Knights weather the storm of barrage bombs that drop amongst the ruins – the Tyranids and Daemons are not so fortunate. When the bombardment ceases, Kai and the surviving Grey Knights evacuate before Daemon and Tyranid reinforcements can arrive, and begin the journey home to Titan to cage the Book of Pandegaras in the Chapter's vaults. The Sky Sentinels begin the Exterminatus that will ravage Sondheim V. In the wake of the Exterminatus, the Sky Sentinels surrender themselves for mindwipe.

The Return to Acralem

Kaldor Draigo returns alone to Acralem to free it from the clutches of M'kar the Reborn, hoping to end the Chapter's ancient feud with the Daemon Prince. Meanwhile, dark forces gather in the warp, and something stirs deep beneath Titan's surface. The Prognosticars are plagued by visions of impending doom, and it seems that the Citadel of Titan itself might face the threat of attack.

Return of the Planet of the Sorcerers

A great shudder ripples through the void as the world of the Thousand Sons, known as the Planet of the Sorcerers, heaves its way back into realspace. Each of the eight Grand Masters consults with the Prognosticars.

Rise of the Primarch

In response to the Prognosticars' visions of destruction on Macragge, Grand Master Voldus rushes to the aid of the empire of Ultramar and witnesses the resurrection of the Primarch, Roboute Guilliman, from his millennia-long stasis. With his fellow Grey Knights, Voldus fights alongside Guilliman during his perilous journey to Holy Terra. Many members of the Primarch's retinue fall, though the Grey Knights stand tall in the fight against the numerous warp Daemons, following Guilliman all the way to the doors of the Emperor's Throne Room.

M41 AGE OF MALEDICTUM

Blackest Night

From the Augurium on Titan comes the combined screams of Prognosticars as the psychic signal of the Cicatrix Maledictum reaches them, mere days before the first warp tears affect realspace. With the Astronomicon extinguished, it is realised that prophetic visions more than six thousand years old are coming to fruition. This grim knowledge is made all the worse by the fact that, as the Great Rift begins to tear open, a rumbling grows stronger and stronger on Titan until the entire moon is beset by ceaseless, ground-splitting quakes. The epicentre of these quakes is deep beneath Mount Anarch, directly below the Chambers of Purity.

The Silent Reprisal

Grey Knights from every brotherhood, along with Paladins and Purifiers, are sent racing to worlds that lie along the seams of the Cicatrix Maledictum. As daemonic hordes spill into realspace, the Grey Knights meet them head on. Through their efforts entire worlds are given time to evacuate and flee the oncoming warp maelstroms, though these heroics go unnoticed by the terrified populations. Across many less fortunate planets where the grip of Chaos has already taken hold, the Grey Knights solemnly set about the task of exterminating billions of Imperial citizens.

Plagues of Ultramar

The Exactors send Strike Force Cautery to Ultramar to aid the Ultramarines and the Ordo Sepulturum in the fight against the Death Guard, who are spreading daemonic plagues across the region. With knowledge of the Heretic Astartes' viral proclivities gleaned from the tomes in the Sanctum Sanctorum, the Grey Knights are able to cripple two vectoriums of the Death Guard's 4th Company and eradicate the Consumptiphagus strain of the Eater Plague.

The Putrid Springs

The 2nd Company of the Scythes of the Emperor, newly reinforced with Primaris battle-brothers, finds itself under siege upon the hive world of Hamagora, assailed by an endless swarm of Nurgle Daemons. Intercessor Squads establish a punishing series of kill-zones amongst the ruins of hive city Agrippa, yet for every Daemon they slay, two more emerge from the dank tunnels of the undercity, and their casualties begin to mount. Operating in total secrecy, Strike Force Harbinger of the 5th Brotherhood teleports into the sub-city. Their quarry is the Great Unclean One Gul'gulm'ga'tol, who has turned Agrippa's sprawling sewage works into his personal baths - hordes of putrid Daemons crawl endlessly forth from the morass of rancid gruel. After a bloody battle, the strike team sends Gul'gulm'ga'tol screaming into the warp. Hamagora is saved, though the Scythes never discover how.

The Brimstone Stampede

The Bloodthirster Xakros'Ka leads his Brimstone Stampede forth from the Great Rift, rampaging across the Carricus Sector and slaughtering trillions of Imperial souls. Rallying the newly founded Storm Reapers Primaris Chapter to their cause, the warriors of the Grey Knights 2nd Brotherhood lead a desperate counter-attack. While the Storm Reapers launch lightning assaults into the flank of Xakros'Ka's mighty horde, the sons of Titan strike at its heart. Armed with the Bloodthirster's true name, they destroy Xakros'Ka's physical form, though the victory comes at a hideous cost.

Draigo and Mortarion

With the Great Rift yawning open and pouring all manner of Chaos monstrosities into realspace, Lord Kaldor Draigo, Supreme Grand Master of the Grey Knights, finds he is able to escape his imprisonment in the warp more frequently and for greater lengths of time. Draigo materialises to aid his battle-brothers in multiple war zones across the Imperium, often turning grim defeat into a decisive victory for the Chapter. Though he quickly fades after each encounter, he imparts to the Grey Knights with whom he fights visions of things to come that he has witnessed within the immaterium. Many of the Prognosticars, seeing the strands of ancient hatred that bind the two together, believe that Draigo's presence is inextricably linked to that of the Daemon Primarch Mortarion.

The Way Forward

With the Grey Knights forces stretched thinner than ever before, Kaldor Draigo appears to each of the Grand Masters and asks their counsel. For the first time in the Chapter's history a particularly dire strategy is given consideration – the Terminus Decree.

LORD KALDOR DRAIGO

SUPREME GRAND MASTER OF THE GREY KNIGHTS

The tale of Kaldor Draigo truly began during the Daemon incursion of the world of Acralem. M'kar the Reborn had led forth a daemonic army from the Realm of Chaos, and would be satisfied with nothing less than the ruin of not only Acralem, but the entire Vidar sector. It was inevitable that the Grey Knights would stand against such a threat. Together with nine regiments of Imperial Guard and Space Marines from the Astral Knights and Flesh Tearers Chapters, the 3rd Brotherhood of the Grey Knights, in whose ranks Draigo fought, descended upon the world.

What awaited was one of the most terrible battles of that century. There can be little doubt that if the Grey Knights had not been there, Acralem would have fallen. The tide was only turned by their daring strike against M'kar's warp-fortress. It was here that Kaldor Draigo, a freshly ennobled battle-brother, made a name for himself. It was Draigo who dealt the deathblow to M'kar, and so cast the daemonic horde back into the warp, but the Daemon clung to life long enough to place a vengeful curse upon his slayer.

'Victory is yours this day mortal, but know that if ever you set foot upon this world again, you and all who follow you shall walk with damnation for ten millennia.'

- M'kar the Reborn to Knight Draigo

Victory on Acralem saw Draigo acclaimed with the rank of Justicar – the first of many such promotions. For two centuries Draigo served his Chapter and Emperor with unfailing distinction. He earned honours and glory unsurpassed by any Grey Knight before him, save perhaps Janus himself, foremost of the founders whose deeds had shaped the Imperium in its darkest times. He became Supreme Grand Master in late M41, following the slaughter of the previous Chapter Lord at the hands of the Daemon Primarch Mortarion, and in the same battle he carved his forebear's name upon Mortarion's rotting heart – an insult that the Daemon has never forgotten. The defeat of the Daemon Primarch was quickly tempered by the dark visions of the Prognosticars. Draigo's ascension to Supreme Grand Master had disturbed the path of fate, though none could foresee the consequences.

Two centuries after Draigo's victory on Acralem, an Astropathic distress beacon brought news to Titan that Acralem had been invaded by Daemons once again. Upon learning of this, Draigo knew without doubt that M'kar had been reborn, and this was the Daemon Prince's attempt to bring true his curse. Having so determined, Draigo gave word forbidding his Chapter to involve themselves with Acralem, lest others fall prey to the doom that was his burden to bear – a duty his battle-brothers bore unwillingly, though, to his knowledge, none disobeyed. Yet the world was not to be abandoned to its fate. Draigo took ship to Acralem, there to meet his unfolding destiny alone.

So it was that Kaldor Draigo, Lord of the Grey Knights, came once again to Acralem. He spoke few words, yet his grim purpose was plain to behold as he trod old battlefields reawakened to fresh slaughter. At the siege of Castle Gorseth it was Draigo who unleashed the psyflame that swept the Daemons away, and he who struck down the plague-rotten abomination that commanded the assault. In the Trebarin Valley, it was Draigo who held rearguard in the narrowest part of the pass, holding the baying hordes of madness at bay whilst the Cadian 912th fell back. Survivors of the retreat recount that Draigo held that rock-strewn corridor for two days, never once missing a blow nor taking a backward step. It would have been hard to judge which side held Lord Kaldor Draigo in the greatest dread – the Daemons, for the crippling losses he had dealt upon their kind, or the soldiers and officers of the Imperial Guard, who saw only a silent brute whose armour was slick with the blood of slain hellspawn.

The confrontation between Draigo and M'kar took place upon the pinnacle of Shadow Peak, before the swirling warp rift from which the Daemon Prince drew his unholy power. As Imperial Guardsmen battled against the braying Daemon hordes, Draigo sought his enemy of old, for he knew M'kar's death would end the Daemon's plans of conquest, just as it had so many years ago.

On the edge of the rift they battled, the Knight and the Daemon, each using every tactic at their command to break the other's guard. The battlefield rang to the sound of their titanic duel, to the clamorous strike of Nemesis sword upon daemonic blade, of silvered steel upon warp metal. The Daemon Prince spat curses and insults at Draigo, but his words and sorceries could find no purchase. Again and again, Draigo summoned the sanctifying flame, yet M'kar merely laughed at the charring of his own flesh, and Draigo could not keep pace with his adversary forever. M'kar's blade glowed darkly with warpflame, and he unleashed a blow mightier than any that had preceded it. The Daemonblade struck home with a dull crack, shattering the Nemesis sword halfway down its length and driving the Grey Knight to one knee. M'kar bellowed with victory, and brandished his blade for the final blow.

However, Draigo was not yet spent. Roaring his own battlecry, he rose up and thrust his sword's severed shard into M'kar's black heart. With that one blow, Draigo delivered Acralem for the second time. As death throes racked M'kar's body, so too did they begin to tear at the warp portal he had summoned. The rift's baleful energies began to disperse and, one by one, the Daemons of his army faded into nothingness. Yet, before the portal closed completely, M'kar had one final act of vengeance. With his last strength, the Daemon Prince cast his talons around Draigo' throat and heaved the Grey Knight into the collapsing rift. So did Kaldor Draigo pass out of the mortal world and into legend.

The tale of Kaldor Draigo did not end that day, as many supposed, for he survived his passage into the Realm of Chaos. Lesser men would have been driven insane by their arrival in the domain of the Chaos Gods, where damnation lurks upon every path. Yet Draigo's mind had long been hardened to the madness and seductions of Chaos, and he somehow endured in this land where no other man could.

For an uncounted age Draigo wandered that terrible, ever-shifting landscape. His path was strewn by Daemons who sought to slay him or seduce him to darkness, yet through bitter struggle Draigo overcame each of them. Atop the Blood Falls, where the acrid ichor of Khorne's fallen champions tumbles endlessly into the void, Draigo slew the great Bloodthirster Kar'voth. With cleansing fire he drove daemonic taint from the beast's great axe, and used the molten remains to reforge his sword, sundered in battle with M'kar the Reborn so long ago. He unleashed sanctified flame again amongst the writhing jungles of Nurgle's domain, and for a long time the gusting warp-winds that buffeted him carried a charcoal stench and the tortured screaming of daemonic vegetation. On a journey through the Whispering Meadows, six sisters, the chosen handmaidens of Slaanesh, sought to tempt Draigo with promises of glory, power and all the myriad riches desired by mortal flesh and spirit, but their words could find no lasting purchase upon his soul, and he scattered the Daemonettes' dismembered remains amongst the alabaster grasses. At the gates of the Inevitable City, the Lord of Change M'kachen offered Draigo a path homewards, but in reply the Grey Knight smote the city walls and left the bird-Daemon entombed amongst the ruins.

However, the mortal world was not yet done with Lord Draigo. When the Prophet of Jostero forged an alliance with the Daemon N'kari, he drew a portion of the Realm of Chaos into the mortal world, and Draigo was drawn through along with it. So was Draigo briefly reunited with his Chapter, for a brotherhood had arrived on Jostero to combat N'kari's threat. Draigo was clearly long adrift in time, for he did not recognise these warriors, yet they embraced him as their brother, and fighting side-by-side they cast down the mad Prophet of Jostero and banished his daemonic allies. Alas, Draigo's victory was a hollow one, for when the gateway closed, the Grey Knight found himself drawn through the rift and trapped again within the warp. He had helped bring about the deliverance of Jostero, but could not save himself. Such has been Draigo's fate ever since: to walk the Realm of Chaos for unknowable periods of time, on occasion taking his eternal battle into the mortal world for brief spans before being freshly jailed upon victory.

Since the Great Rift tore the Imperium asunder, Kaldor Draigo has found his way back into realspace more and more frequently. Some of the Grand Masters believe that, as the Cicatrix Maledictum shredded the veil between reality and the warp, so did it weaken the bonds that tether Draigo to the Chaos realm. Others believe that the forces of Chaos that occluded the Supreme Grand Master's vision are now dispersed across dimensions, and thus Kaldor Draigo can perceive the needs of those he leads across the vastness of the galaxy. Regardless of reason, one thing is certain – Draigo has appeared to aid his Grey Knights multiple times since the opening of the rift. He has even been witnessed fighting in different war zones on opposite sides of the galaxy. Perhaps the opening of the rift will allow his return – or perhaps it will seal his fate forever. The Prognosticars are divided on this matter. Draigo himself does not spend his time musing over such issues. He uses what little time he has hunting down the foul spawn that the rift has regurgitated. Chief amongst his quarries is his enemy of old – the Daemon Primarch Mortarion, the murderer of his predecessor.

THE TITANSWORD

A relic of the earliest days of the Imperium, the Titansword has been entrusted to the Supreme Grand Master of the Grey Knights since records began. Stories of the force blade give it many names: Mind's Edge, Foebane and Lifedrinker to name a few. Legends say the Emperor forged the blade for a favoured general during the Unification Wars on Terra, teaching him how to use his mind to trigger its terrible powers. During the Great Crusade it then passed into the hands of his champions, spilling alien blood on a hundred worlds as Mankind reclaimed the stars.

When Malcador the Sigillite took the first Grey Knights to Titan, one of the relics he carried with him was rumoured to be the ancient force sword. Along with his pure genetic legacy and psychic power, it was one of the Emperor's gifts to the newly founded Chapter. Renamed the Titansword by Janus, the first Supreme Grand Master, the blade must be psychically attuned to each new master. Only once it is keyed to the mind of the wielder can its true killing power be called upon.

The Titansword is more than a mere weapon – it is the badge of office of the Supreme Grand Master, a potent symbol of the Chapter's sacred duty and the Emperor's fury given form. Every lord of the Chapter has been the warden of this blade, and though many have used other weapons in battle, the Titansword's keen blade has slain more foul Daemons than any other.

GRAND MASTER VOLDUS

WARDEN OF THE LIBRARIUS

Aldrik Voldus, Grand Master of the Wardmakers, wields more psychic might than any Grey Knight seen in centuries. The very air crackles around him as he focuses his mind and bends the colossal energies of the warp to his will. With a word, purifying flames pour forth from the head of his ornate Nemesis Daemon hammer – the Malleus Argyrum – turning Chaos-tainted flesh, bone and armour into pillars of ash. Heretic war engines shudder and halt as their twisted machine spirits are rent from their chassis. In Voldus' grip reality constricts, and the helms of his enemies are crushed by invisible waves of force. Just as easily he can focus the minds of his fellow Grey Knights, allowing them to strike true at their foes amidst the fog of war, or channel their physical reserves into strikes that can fell all but the largest of Daemons. Voldus himself is also a dauntless fighter, having battled in strike forces with the 3rd Brotherhood on not one, but two Daemon worlds within the Eye of Terror. With every deft swing of the perfectly balanced Malleus Argyrum Voldus shatters those before him. The boom of thunder sounds with each strike as channelled psychic energies are unleashed upon his victims.

It was only at the onset of the Gathering Storm that Voldus was made Grand Master of the 3rd Brotherhood and Warden of the Librarius. The position is renowned for being dangerous, and perhaps even cursed. The previous Warden, Doriam Narathem, was only recently promoted to Grand Master at the time of his death, and during his fourth mission in this role led the Wardmakers to a daemonic incursion on the fortress world of Longhallow to extract the precious relics held there. When the Lord of Change M'kachen tore from the warp into realspace and slew Narathem, it was Brother Voldus who unleashed the full force of his psychic power on the Greater Daemon. Perhaps guided by the pure empyric light, Grand Master Kaldor Draigo emerged from the immaterium and joined the battle. With their wills united, the two Grey Knights banished M'kachen, sending him writhing back beyond the veil.

In the wake of the battle, Draigo himself appointed the humble Voldus to the rank of Grand Master, lauding his exceptional heroism and psychic prowess. Even as Draigo's curse took hold and he began to fade from realspace, Voldus swore an oath to live up to this great honour – one of which he did not truly believe himself worthy. He strives towards this goal in all his actions, offering prayers to the Emperor of Mankind for strength and guidance.

Since taking up the mantle of Grand Master, Voldus has been instrumental in guiding the actions of the Grey Knights. After consulting with the Prognosticars, Voldus and a small strike force rushed to Macragge to aid the Ultramarines in what would come to be known as the Siege of Hera. These warriors would bear witness to a miracle of faith and technology – the resurrection of Roboute Guilliman. Voldus and his battle-brothers fought side by side with the Primarch against the legions of Heretic Astartes on Macragge. They slew Daemons and traitors across the reaches of space, through the twisting paths of the webway and on the surface of Luna. Voldus even accompanied Guilliman to Holy Terra, to the doors of the Emperor's Throne Room. In his brief tenure, Voldus has played a greater part in the fate of the Imperium than perhaps any other living Grand Master.

GRAND MASTERS

As one of the Chapter's finest and most revered warriors, a Grand Master's duty is to take charge of those battles so pivotal or perilous that even the hardened warrior-skills of a Brother-Captain are deemed insufficient to the task at hand. Such a campaign is sure to see the Grey Knights at the very pinnacle of their abilities, for a Grand Master has a keen eye for strategy, and an uncanny skill for ensuring his troops fight at peak efficiency. Under a Grand Master's guiding will, a Grey Knights strike force will often adopt non-standard doctrines with a precision and speed that is nothing short of uncanny. Indeed, it is said by some that a Grand Master is apt to control his subordinates' minds if it will bring victory; others claim it is simply the hallmark of a remarkable leader.

A Grand Master is himself a paragon of battle, unleashing righteous fury upon all who stand before him. Every blow from his Nemesis weapon carries with it the immense weight of his full psychic potential, and with the ease of breathing he delivers bolts of crackling energy and streams of storm bolter shells into the foe.

By tradition, there are eight Grand Masters of the Grey Knights. Each is the spiritual heir of one of the eight founding Grand Masters. To reach this rank is to have battled on ten thousand worlds, to have slain Daemons unnumbered and to have stood stalwart as an unfailing example of honour and purity, not only to your battle-brothers, but to every soul in the Imperium. Even then, a new Grand Master can only be appointed by the will of those whose ranks he would join. Before he can be raised, those already established must be unanimous in approval.

Each of the Grand Masters commands the might of an entire brotherhood, wielding the Grey Knight battle-brothers they oversee like a blade of purest silver. Though a Brother-Captain, Librarian or Chaplain may be charged with leading a strike force to battle, it is a brotherhood's Grand Master who maps out and prosecutes the unending war against the denizens of the warp. By consulting with the Prognosticars and heeding their visions, a Grand Master can determine where his forces are most needed. But even with such guidance, the decisions that come before a Grand Master are painfully difficult. The Grey Knights are small in number and the Imperium is vast. Not all worlds can be saved from Daemons, and like rotting limbs some must be severed, whereas others must be preserved no matter how high the cost. It is a heavy burden, and the Grand Masters answer to none for their actions save their fellows and the Supreme Grand Master.

To ensure the effectiveness of their forces, a Grand Master also holds responsibility for maintaining his brotherhood's many alliances, whether with other organisations within the Imperium, or the various alien races with whom the Grey Knights have covert dealings. The actual detail of such treaties, pacts and accords are worked out by the Chapter's scribes – a warrior's time is too precious to be expended on such bureaucratic detail. The Grand Master's chief role in these matters is to attend the occasion in full regalia of war. It is rarely necessary for him to speak in order to convey the will of his brotherhood – his grim and martial aspect are a stark warning to any who would think to abuse the Chapter's trust.

> **'Today's ally is merely tomorrow's traitor. We will be watching you.'**
>
> *- Grand Master Agraveld Tor speaking at the Antares Conclave*

PALADIN SQUADS

The Grey Knights do not believe that a warrior is forged in battle; rather that war tempers the fighting spirit of a man born to great things. Therefore, if a Grey Knight wishes to prove himself worthy of a place amongst the Paladins, bravery and skill are not enough – he must complete eight quests to establish his character and cause.

First, the aspirant must spend a day and a night in the haunted caverns beneath Mount Anarch without losing sanity or purpose. Should he endure, he must match his will against the unsleeping evil of the dread tome Abbiallach, which lies chained in the Chapter's Sanctum Sanctorum. His mental fortitude thus tested, the aspirant will then be called upon to prove his strength at arms.

He will make pilgrimage to Lansel's Tomb on the doomed moon of Tethys, bearing no armour to preserve him from the warp-spawned beasts trapped there. He must seek out and deliver a deathblow to each of the four types of Daemon Herald in service to the Chaos Gods, returning with a horn or tooth from each to prove his victory. Four more quests are there, each more gruelling than the last, with the final one the most difficult of all. The candidate will hunt down and banish one of the six hundred and sixty-six most powerful Daemons to ever manifest in the mortal realm, armed only with his Nemesis force sword and the beast's true name, gleaned from the pages of the Iron Grimoire. Only when this is done will the aspirant have earned his ascension to the rank of Paladin.

Given the perilous nature of these quests, it is little wonder that only the boldest Knights become Paladins. Most Grey Knights who set out on this path are eventually slain or sucked wholly into the warp by the myriad Daemons they hunt. Nevertheless, it is almost unheard of for an aspirant to abandon his quests, as to do so is to incur grave dishonour. Whilst the cost of pursuing the Paladin's quests is high, it ensures that nowhere in the Imperium can so noble an assemblage of warriors be found as in Titan's Hall of Champions.

Once his quests are complete, and the night of triumphant feasting is over, the new Paladin leaves his brotherhood and takes his seat in that hallowed hall. From the moment of his elevation, each Paladin is bound in service not only to his Chapter, but also to one of the Grand Masters for whom he will act as bodyguard, champion and advisor. This last role is possibly the most valuable to the Grand Masters, for even amongst the Grey Knights there are few with such extensive first-hand knowledge of the true dangers the Chapter must face.

Once a battle-brother becomes a Paladin, his place in war will henceforth be wherever the fighting is thickest and the peril greatest. Without a moment's hesitation, a Paladin will hurl himself into combat with towering Greater Daemons and hordes of swarming warp-creatures. He has fought mightier foes before and lived, so such an enemy has no ability to command fear in him. An entire squad of Paladins is a near impenetrable bulwark formed of the Chapter's staunchest and most skilled warriors. They will readily manoeuvre to defend others on the battlefield, allowing an Apothecary to carry out their duty of preserving the Chapter's gene-seed or escorting a Librarian into the heart of a burgeoning daemonic incursion.

CHAPLAINS

To see a Chaplain in combat is to behold the true face of the Angels of Death. Adorned with ornate sigils and crowned with a skull death mask, a Chaplain is a symbol of brutal mortality and unquestioning zeal. Their presence on the battlefield breeds fear in their enemies and inspires their fellow battle-brothers to ever greater acts of righteous violence. They are the speakers of the Emperor's word and a living reminder to other Space Marines that, though the flesh may die, the immortal soul and the legacy of the Chapter must be preserved.

Chaplains are the spiritual leaders of their Chapter. Within the Grey Knights, the Chaplains lead their battle-brothers in prayer at great gatherings in the Hall of Champions. New recruits receive tutelage in the Chapter's strictures and dicta through a Chaplain's fervently bellowed litanies, and it is the Chaplains who administer merciless – and often fatal – discipline to those who question or waver in their dedication. None save the Supreme Grand Master himself holds more authority than a Chaplain in ensuring the purity of each battle-brother's soul.

A Chaplain's duty is doubly important on the battlefield, where they physically embody the sacred duty of the Adeptus Astartes. Recruits and veterans alike face down insidious Daemons that can exploit even the slightest weakness in a Grey Knight's defences. Just a momentary lapse of willpower – brought on by the searing pain of warpfire or from witnessing the death of a renowned warrior – is enough for many entities to penetrate a battle-brother's psychic shielding, to rip his soul from his body or flay him alive. The cost of this dereliction is one the Chapter simply cannot bear. No matter the circumstances, and regardless of how dire the situation, the impassioned canticles of a Chaplain ring loud and pure through the clangour of battle. By attuning his mind to that of his followers, a Grey Knights Chaplain can commune psychically with his followers, ensuring the litanies suffer no interruption. His every utterance carries with it the sanctified truth of a Grey Knight's purpose. Each verse he recites is a gift from the Emperor, as vital to the brothers in his flock as their storm bolters and Nemesis weapons. By these words do they steel themselves against the enemy.

This solidarity of mind and soul is then turned brutally upon those who stand before the Grey Knights. A Chaplain's intoned execrations cause the blood of each warrior near him to boil with focused fury, unleashing the disciplined wrath that is seeded deep within them. To a Grey Knights Chaplain, the six hundred and sixty-six verses of contempt are tools with which he can tap the latent passion and vigour that is hypno-indocrinated into each battle-brother during his creation. His words sharpen the hatred of those he leads so that they may inflict the most devastating blows against their enemies.

Chaplains are themselves fearsome warriors, and are often drawn from the most spiritually pure members of the Paladins. They wield a crozius arcanum, which acts as both their rod of office and their weapon of preference. With each mighty strike of this ornate mace, surges of crackling energy tear through the flesh, armour and bone of their foes.

ROSARIUS

Emblazoned on a Chaplain's breastplate or hung around his neck, a rosarius contains a conversion field generator which amplifies the spiritual will of the wearer into a physical shield of energy. A rosarius bears the symbol of the aquila or a Crux Terminatus and – unlike most artefacts of the Grey Knights – is bestowed upon a Chaplain by the Ecclesiarchy of Terra, who believe it to be a projector of the Emperor's divine power. The Grey Knights have never viewed the Emperor as a god – but they know full well that it is through his supreme will and genetic heritage that they are able to stand in purity against the Dark Gods of Chaos.

CASTELLAN CROWE

CHAMPION OF THE ORDER OF PURIFIERS

Castellan Garran Crowe is both head and Brotherhood Champion of the Purifier order. A nobler exemplar of the Grey Knights would be impossible to find – by the measure of the Grey Knights, Crowe is a flawless soul, so resistant to the temptations of Chaos as to be all but immune to them. It is well that this is so, for Garran bears a burden greater than any of his brothers – the Black Blade of Antwyr.

The Grey Knights first encountered the Blade of Antwyr during the latter years of M37. It was one of the many horrors unleashed upon the galaxy during the mad years of the Occlusiad, unearthed from amongst the ruins of an ancient temple by apostles of the Blind King. A Daemon weapon of great power, the Blade of Antwyr swiftly corrupted its discoverer's mind and body. Together, sword and slave made bloody war upon the Vidar, Tremayne and Darkspire sectors, a war only ended by the intercession of all eight brotherhoods of Grey Knights. In the aftermath of that great conflict, the Blade and its wielder vanished into the warp. Yet seldom is such evil gone forever, and three thousand years later, on the doomed moon of Tethys, the Blade of Antwyr crossed the path of the Grey Knights once more. This time, however, its bearer was finally slain, and the sword that had once nearly doomed the galaxy now lay in the hands of its enemies.

Alas, the Grey Knights were unable to destroy the Blade of Antwyr. Its warp-spawned form was impervious to all means at their disposal. Yet they were reluctant to cast the evil sword into the darkness of interstellar space, for they felt certain that a fresh bearer would be drawn to its evil. Similarly, to seal it away in a vault would simply be to invite corruption of the chamber's guardians. So was the decision made to place the Blade of Antwyr into the safest prison of which the Grey Knights could conceive. It was given over into the wardenship of the Purifiers, who in turn placed the blade into the hands of their Brotherhood Champion. So has the Blade passed from incorruptible warrior to incorruptible warrior for a thousand years, and has now reached the hands of Garran Crowe.

Crowe's wardenship of the Blade of Antwyr has brought him both physical and spiritual peril. When not beset by the maddened mortals and desperate Daemons drawn by the sword's evil, Crowe must do psychic battle with the Blade itself, for it strives ever to tempt him with promises of power or bind his will with the blackest sorceries. Tendrils of iridescent energy leap from its edges, scorching flesh and melting metal with their baleful caress. With every crackling surge Crowe is reminded of the destruction the blade could bring to his enemies.

Crowe must be forever on guard, for the sword's sibilant whispers echo endlessly through his mind, offering to lend its strength to his own in the pursuit of victory. Many men would embrace such a chance, gambling that their will would be strong enough to control the sword's bounty without becoming corrupted in return. Yet no matter how dark the hour or desperate the battle, Crowe has never succumbed – his thoughts and actions are his own. He is the guardian of the Blade, incorruptible and inviolable, and will remain so until the day of his death.

PURIFIER SQUADS

The Purifiers are an order apart from other Grey Knights, distanced from their battle-brothers by their nature and tradition. The Chambers of Purity lie deep below the fortress monastery, at the entrance to the ancient and shadowy vaults of Mount Anarch, the better to ensure that the Purifiers guard against the evil that slumbers therein. Only the Chapter's Grand Masters are permitted to enter these halls unbidden. This edict has proved something of a challenge to neophytes over the centuries. Some return to the chambers above following a brutal beating to reinforce the lesson that the Purifiers trust not even their battle-brothers where some secrets are concerned. Other intruders do not return at all, their fate a mystery to all.

> ***'To the righteous we bring hope. To the tainted we bring fire.'***
>
> *- Castellan Garran Crowe*

Just as the Paladins serve as exemplars of the Grey Knights' warrior ideal, the Purifiers epitomise the Chapter's sanctity of purpose. They are dour and taciturn, and their eyes burn with a black fire that borders on fanaticism. There is neither training regime nor set process by which a Grey Knight can join these ranks. Membership of the Purifier order is not granted through skill, valour or a tally of grim deeds soaked in blood. Indeed, a Grey Knight can serve his Chapter with distinction for centuries without end, yet still this ultimate honour may well be denied him. Rather, Purifiers recruit only from those amongst their battle-brothers whose souls are considered to be utterly incorruptible and resistant to the temptations of the warp – even by the exacting standards of the Grey Knights. So careful is the selection that there are seldom more than a handful of Purifiers. Yet never has thought been given to relaxing the restrictions of induction, lest the sanctity of the order be compromised.

Throughout the Chapter's history, the limited numbers of Purifiers have never yet been too few for the task at hand. Whether this is due to some strange quirk of fate or the machinations of some higher power is impossible to say. Perhaps it is part of the Emperor's will for there to exist a few unblemished warriors, whose purpose is to combat Daemons in all their forms and to ensure that the fire of victory is never extinguished. Perhaps it is by the designs of some darker power that so few have the resilience of spirit to take up their mantle. In any case, the Purifiers often form the Chapter's spearhead against the legions of Daemons who pour from the Cicatrix Maledictum. As with all Grey Knights, they never question their duty.

An untarnished spirit is not simply the Purifiers' defining characteristic – it is also their greatest weapon. Combined with a Grey Knight's formidable psychic might, this hallowness of heart and mind can be transformed into a cleansing azure fire that burns both the body and soul of an unworthy adversary. Any source of evil draws the flame, and few dark creatures can resist the power of this glorious conflagration. A Daemon's cold malevolence is turned violently against it, a corrupted soldier's fear erupts into a corona of fire. None save the Purifiers walk unharmed through this blaze, armour gleaming as they dispatch their charred and blackened foes.

BROTHER-CAPTAIN STERN

BANE OF M'KACHEN

Arvann Stern ranks amongst the Grey Knights' longest-serving and most highly decorated Brother-Captains. So well-regarded and valorous is Stern that, even from his early career he was thought to be firmly on the path to becoming one of the Grand Masters. Alas, his service in the Chapter was to take an altogether different course.

When the Cult of the Red Talon arose on Antraxes at the command of their daemonic master, the Lord of Change M'kachen, it was Stern who led the counter-attack. Striking at the heart of the cult's temple, Stern and his battle-brothers held true to their quest. Though outnumbered, the Grey Knights slaughtered the cultists to the final damned soul. At the last, even the mighty M'kachen was defeated, banished screaming back into the warp by Stern himself – a formidable feat normally thought beyond the psychic abilities of a lone Brother-Captain. From that moment, Stern's fate was to be forever intertwined with that of the Tzeentchian Daemon, for M'kachen vowed to devour Stern's mortal soul, even if it took him until the end of time.

So began a vendetta as yet without end. One-hundred and one years since his banishment, M'kachen entered realspace once again. Possessing the body of an unwitting cultist, he wasted no time in laying a trap for Stern among the obsidian pyramids of Sargotha. Of the five Grey Knights who set foot on Sargotha, only Stern survived the ambush. He now bears on his face and body the scars from that battle amidst the blinding sands. M'kachen escaped from the fray unharmed.

Stern and M'kachen have fought many times since that day. On each occasion, the Daemon has fled the field, though not before slaughtering Stern's companions, often leaving the Brother-Captain as the sole survivor. It is unclear to Stern, the Council of Grand Masters and even the Prognosticars if M'kachen is toying with him, or if the Brother-Captain is simply too difficult a prey for the Daemon. M'kachen appears to interfere in Stern's fate almost constantly – for every act of heroism and bravery that Stern performs in battle, he seems to invite some inexplicable misfortune also.

Despite the considerable cost to the Grey Knights, these confrontations can hardly be considered a victory for the Daemon, as they always end in his retreat. On each occasion that Stern battles his nemesis, the Brother-Captain garners fresh knowledge of M'kachen's weaknesses, fuelling his hope that the Daemon will one day meet a permanent defeat – either cast back into the warp, or sealed within the technological prison of a tesseract labyrinth. This is why Stern constantly trains and prepares, refusing promotion to the rank of Grand Master until the threat of M'kachen can be ended forever.

For their part, the Grey Knights of Stern's brotherhood support him unflinchingly – duty and honour extinguishing any mortal fear they might hold. One day, they feel sure M'kachen will over-reach himself, and on that day it will be the sword of Arvann Stern that avenges the Grey Knights' fallen. So has he sworn, and so shall it be done.

TRIALS OF UNDYING ENMITY

The Harrowing

Stern leads Strike Force Arbalest in search of M'kachen on the daemonically shrouded world of Gharelghast. After six days fighting in total darkness, the planet is scoured of Daemons, and all but three of Stern's battle-brothers are slain.

Face of Duplicity

The Prognosticars see visions of M'kachen appearing on two worlds– Voltikron III and Michar's Meadow. With only time to save one, Stern sets off to the most vital planet immediately, but upon arriving at Michar's Meadow he finds an untouched agri-world. Mere days later, the loss of Voltikron III to a Tzeentchian cult is reported.

Fractured Prism

After his forces are overrun by M'kachen's cohorts, Stern faces the Lord of Change alone in the Mirrorstone Mines. Many times does Stern strike down his foe only to realise that it was one of the Greater Daemon's disguised minions. When but one Daemon remains, the true M'kachen flees.

BROTHER-CAPTAINS

Brother-Captains stand amongst the Chapter's foremost warriors, and are second only in rank and battle experience to the Grand Masters themselves. Each has proven his worth time and again, both as a leader of battle-brothers and as a fearsome fighter in his own right. Brother-Captains are almost exclusively appointed from the ranks of the Chapter's Paladins, for only these most experienced of warriors can be said to display both the martial and strategic skills that a Captain must master. Furthermore, a Brother-Captain is likely to have begun his service within the brotherhood to which he is appointed, for to lead he must know intrinsically the rites, practices and combat specialities of those he leads. That said, exceptions have been made for particularly valorous and capable battle-brothers from all facets of the Chapter, for the Grey Knights are nothing if not pragmatic. Procedure and tradition are all very well, but it is the mission and the might of the Chapter that truly matter.

Upon the battlefield, a Brother-Captain's place is in the very heart of the fighting, for what example can he set for his battle-brothers unless he stands shoulder-to-shoulder with them? Yet even while the Captain strikes at the enemy with storm bolter and Nemesis force weapon, his mind is set to directing his forces towards the greater victory. Indeed, as part of his training, a Brother-Captain will learn how to make psychic contact with his warriors, even amidst the din of furious battle. Those Grey Knights in his presence feel a stillness of spirit and clarity of vision, and from this meditative state of purity they unleash unadulterated psychic destruction upon their enemies.

Each Brother-Captain has authority over an entire brotherhood of Grey Knights, and thus has under his command multiple squads of the galaxy's finest warriors. In matters of strategy and planning, a Captain answers to no-one, not even to the Grand Masters. His is a heavy responsibility, and one undertaken with sombre dignity. To command a brotherhood of the Grey Knights is to command power itself, and in lesser organisations, unrestrained control of such power could, and often does, lead to the corruption of the individual in question. Yet a Brother-Captain of the Grey Knights is above such things. After all, when one's soul is hardened against the promises and blandishments proffered by Daemons, then mere mortal temptations are easily set aside.

By his deeds, each Brother-Captain will have earned honours and titles other than his formal rank – honours that carry so much weight that their full meaning cannot be captured by a battle-brother's heraldry alone. Some of these are traditional to the Chapter, others are unique, awarded by the Grand Masters for acts of valour, and by their form serve as a truncated history of that warrior's achievements. So it is that a long-serving Brother-Captain may be known by half a dozen or more titles. None have accrued so many as Aldar the Bold, whose traditional title of 'Keeper of the Light' has been supplemented by no less than a score of other honorifics, of which 'Slayer of the Bloodbeast' can be considered the least, and 'Liberator of the Solipsis Sector' is by far the most prestigious. Whilst such a lengthy roster of honours can lead to ponderous moments at the Grey Knights' high feasts – when each Captain's titles must be announced in full – they stand as an important example of duty and heroism to all the Chapter's battle-brothers.

> ***'Why should I fear the Daemon? He has no power over me.'***
>
> *- Brother-Captain Castavor Drak*

LIBRARIANS

All Grey Knights recruits have some latent psychic talent. It is for this reason that they were selected for the Chapter. Their inherent power is then honed through training and battle until it is a powerful weapon. But few battle-brothers exercise this power with free rein. For most, careful practice and supervision allows them to focus their abilities in concert with those of their battle-brothers. However, those who prove to have a strength of mind far greater than that of their fellows will go on to join the ranks of the Chapter's Librarians.

Grey Knights Librarians have a will of iron. They must, for they court the dangers of the warp even more than their fellows. While most Grey Knights will master a single incantation to great effect, a Librarian's knowledge is much more diverse. The further one's mind reaches into the warp, the brighter it shines, acting as a beacon to the predatory evils that lurk there. To allow the slightest wavering of concentration, even a momentary weaknesses of spirit, is to offer oneself up body and soul to those otherworldly hunters and to eternal damnation beyond.

On the battlefield, Librarians typically use their powers to support their battle-brothers, summoning them across the battlefield, cloaking them in protective shadows, or imbuing them with strength. Yet they are also capable of wreaking great devastation, opening a roiling vortex that tears at a Daemon's mortal form or smiting their enemies with a bolt of eldritch lightning.

As well as being able to unleash arcane powers, all Grey Knights are adept at resisting the malefic energies of their foes. Librarians possess even greater defences, turning aside the insidious influences of Chaos as if they were nothing more than foul air.

Little is beyond a Librarian, for in the Sanctum Sanctorum is recorded every sigil of power and incantation known throughout the Imperium, and it is from these tomes that the Librarian draws his knowledge – though most of the evocations contained there are far too dangerous and volatile to be put to use.

Yet for all the contributions a Librarian can make to a Grey Knights strike force, his most vital tasks are carried out within the walls of the fortress monastery on Titan. It is here that the Librarian schools new recruits in the mysteries that all Grey Knights must know: the six chants of denial, the seven words of life and death, the eight songs of battle, the nine terrible powers that form the basis of all disciplines and much more besides.

A Librarian's tutelage is a most rigorous process, and many aspirants do not survive. Yet if the Librarians are called upon to be ruthless, there is little cruelty in their actions, and no malice. This culling of the weak is merely a necessity – for the Grey Knights to remain incorruptible, they must be as hard of mind and will as they are of body.

A few Librarians are fortunate enough to reach an age when their bodies can no longer meet the rigours of campaign. Such warriors are removed from the Chapter's fighting roster entirely, and retire to the labyrinthine corridors of the Sanctum Sanctorum to take up guardianship of its crypts. Only these ancient ones know the full catalogue, for there are some secrets buried therein of which even the Grand Masters are ignorant. Such mysteries can never be allowed to escape the confines of the Sanctum Sanctorum, for the fear is ever that even some amongst the Grey Knights would not prove immune to their temptations.

APOTHECARIES

So few are the Grey Knights, and so numerous the horrors they must face, that each is an invaluable weapon of their Chapter, and it is to the Apothecaries that the vital task of healing wounded battle-brothers falls. Amidst enemy hordes, under hails of fire and blasts of daemonic energy, an Apothecary sets about their duty, hastily using the tools of their narthecium to bring the fallen back from the brink of death. While unleashing psychic blasts and slicing at oncoming foes with their Nemesis force sword, they excise bullets and splintered daemonic claws from the flesh of their brethren. After cauterising gaping lacerations, they use stimulant injectors to rouse the wounded once more to battle, enabling them to overcome even the most grievous injuries as they rejoin the fight.

Wherever possible, Apothecaries will accompany members of their Chapter into combat. A single Apothecary can have the same impact on a battle as a dozen Grey Knights, transforming a close-fought and costly bloodbath into a decisive victory. However, there are some injuries that a Space Marine – even those with the additional conditioning of the Grey Knights – cannot survive. The most hideous denizens of the warp can tear the spine of a Grey Knight in two with their massive claws or, with gouts of superheated hellfire, reduce flesh and armour to little more than ash and slag. It is when a Grey Knight is so badly wounded that no recovery is possible, or when he is slain outright, that the Apothecary is truly needed.

With his warrior brother lying dead or dying before him, the Apothecary uses the serrated blade of his reductor to saw an incision in the black carapace of the fallen. Then, with grim precision, the Apothecary plunges the acicular spike of the reductor into the body of the Space Marine. Whatever life remained ebbs quickly as the reductor extracts the progenoid glands from the chest and neck. Progenoid glands are specialised bio-implant organs found in every Space Marine, and are the most precious resource of any Chapter. They create the germ cells known as gene-seed needed to mould new recruits into mighty Adeptus Astartes. This is the lifeblood of the Grey Knights, and is their genetic link to the Emperor himself. By harvesting the gene-seed of the fallen, Apothecaries ensure the survival of the entire Chapter, even if an individual battle-brother may die.

Once a Grey Knight has received honours enough to become an Apothecary, they are trained in advanced combat triage and taught the sacred rites of creating new Adeptus Astartes using harvested gene-seed by the Chapter's existing Apothecaries. Unlike those in most Space Marines Chapters, Grey Knights Apothecaries learn a series of ritual blessings that are performed on every bio-implant to form an enduring ward against daemonic incursion.

Due to the importance of their duty, Apothecaries are typically well-defended on the field of battle, with others of their brotherhood forming a shield around them. But this is not to say that they shy away from combat. On the contrary, for not only are they themselves fully-fledged Grey Knights, but exemplars to whom the grave burden of protecting the Chapter's gene-seed has been entrusted. As proficient with their blades as any from their Chapter, and a powerful psyker in their own right, Apothecaries are formidable assets in the fight against Chaos.

NARTHECIUM

The narthecium is the med-pack used to deliver emergency ministrations and life-saving chem-injections to fallen Grey Knights, and is the most important tool of an Apothecary. It includes arrays of scanning occulums and augularium fonts to diagnose the extent of any injury. Though all Space Marine Apothecaries utilise a narthecium, those employed by the Grey Knights have been tailored to the Chapter's specific needs and are amongst the finest and most elaborate in the Imperium – they must be in order to counter the effects of the horrendous and insidious weapons used against them. If a battle-brother is cut by the wretched blade of a Nurglesque plaguesword, an Apothecary can locate and purge the daemonic infections that quickly begin coursing through flesh and bodily fluids. Similarly, the bursts of pink and blue flame spat forth by Tzeentchian Daemons can cause internal combustion as the blood begins to boil, yet a swift application of atomised thrice-blessed water can halt the infernal mutations. Most importantly, a Grey Knights Apothecary's narthecium contains salves and unguents that have been psychically blessed by the Purifiers to remove all trace of daemonic taint from a battle-brother's wounds, for it is said that without purity of spirit, a Grey Knight's life has no purpose.

ANCIENTS

There are very few places in the Imperium that record the heroics of the Grey Knights Chapter. Even amongst the Adeptus Astartes there exist only whispered rumours. This is a necessity, for though the deeds of the Chapter are great and their victories many, knowledge of the war they wage carries with it great danger – to know the purpose of the Grey Knights' existence is to know far too much of the Daemon threat. The only true record of the Chapter's history exists on Titan, etched into the statues and woven into the banners that reside within the Hall of Champions. These memorials tell stories of countless unspoken victories and extol fallen luminaries so that their names may continue to inspire new generations of warriors. Some of these are borne to war by Ancients – battle-brothers who, through centuries of unfaltering courage and constancy, have earned the honour of holding aloft one of these hallowed banners in combat.

An Ancient dedicates their efforts in battle to holding high their Chapter's banner, and in the shadow of the sacred standard those brothers around him are roused to even greater feats of heroism. In the darkest moments of hellish conflict, when a strike force is horrendously out-gunned and outnumbered, the Ancient invokes the names and deeds recorded on his banner. With every utterance the warriors in his presence are emboldened, for the Ancient's words tell the truth of the Grey Knights – they are the descendants of the Emperor's greatest champions, his perfect weapons against the corruption of the warp. By their hand have all manner of foes been slain with bolt and blade and psychic fury.

Only the most steadfast Grey Knights become Ancients, for the banner they carry is an irreplaceable heirloom of their Chapter, and they must fight to protect it past the point where others would succumb to fatigue and injury. Those who do become Ancients are often trusted advisors within a brotherhood, having served several Brother-Captains or even Grand Masters. Greatest and most revered of all are the Paladin Ancients, for they have fought through many of the battles recorded on the banners they bear.

Each banner holds more than mere words and images of past victories. The silver thread with which they are woven is sanctified through rites of purification as it is spun and blessed with wards to protect against warp energies. So pristine is every strand that some brotherhoods believe each banner contains the psychic resonance of the very battle-brothers whose stories it tells.

This banner belongs to the 2nd Brotherhood, and is just one of many that the Blades of Victory carry into war. It depicts purifiying flame burning daemonic corruption from the galaxy.

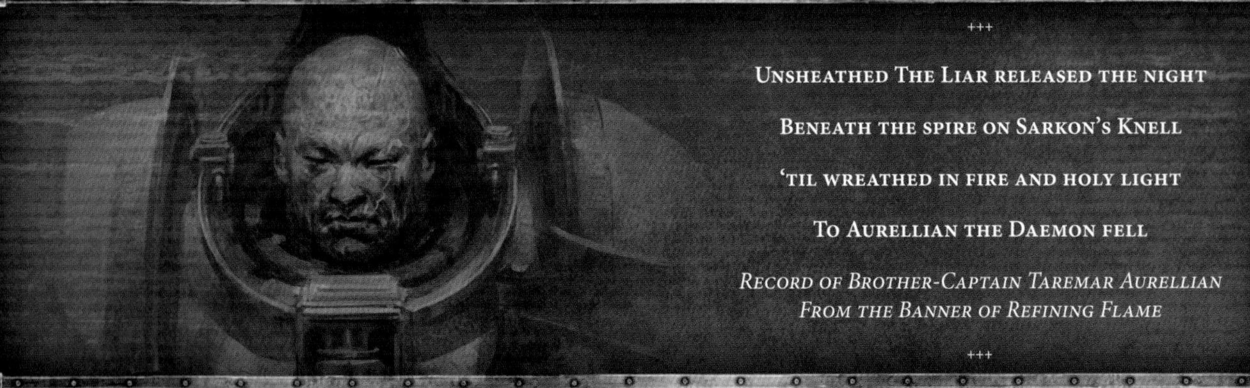

+++

UNSHEATHED THE LIAR RELEASED THE NIGHT

BENEATH THE SPIRE ON SARKON'S KNELL

'TIL WREATHED IN FIRE AND HOLY LIGHT

TO AURELLIAN THE DAEMON FELL

RECORD OF BROTHER-CAPTAIN TAREMAR AURELLIAN
FROM THE BANNER OF REFINING FLAME

+++

BROTHERHOOD CHAMPIONS

Where a Grand Master dictates the strategy of a brotherhood in its unending mission, and a Brother-Captain leads his battle-brothers on the fields of war, a Brotherhood Champion acts as an exemplar of divine martial prowess to which all Grey Knights aspire. He is a warrior of peerless skill, having reached the apex of training with every weapon in the Chapter's armoury. Fighting at the fore of battles against the largest and most horrendous monstrosities, a Brotherhood Champion perfectly embodies the discipline and might of the Grey Knights.

The Nemesis force sword is the weapon of choice amongst Brotherhood Champions, for above all other armaments a sword allows for both offensive and defensive manoeuvres. Against myriad foes a Brotherhood Champion may set their stance wide, putting even greater strength into every slash and stab of his blade. Conversely, when facing down some ancient horror from the warp he will remain light on his feet, nimbly feinting and parrying the creatures' attacks.

Among a Brotherhood Champion's responsibilities are the martial training of new recruits, and on the battlefield he acts as bodyguard to his Brother-Captain. Each Champion stands ready to die in his Captain's stead. That said, few opponents stand any chance of breaking a Brotherhood Champion's guard, let alone surviving his vengeful return strike. Should a Champion be struck down, his willpower coalesces as a pulse of psychic energy released into his Aegis suit, giving him one final burst of energy and the opportunity to strike one last blow for his battle-brothers.

The stench permeating the frigate was thickest just outside the bridge. As the blast door groaned open a mountain of writhing filth heaved forward. Feydor Ankhalas, Brotherhood Champion of the Silver Blades, sidestepped the Daemon Prince Offalrott and arced his blade to deflect the swipe of a colossal claw. Ankhalas and his fellow Grey Knights had battled waves of putrid Daemons to reach the Nurglesque monster. Now only he remained, having ordered his battle-brothers off the vessel before it was sucked into the warp-tear. Offalrott stabbed out with his other taloned hand, but again Ankhalas parried before plunging his sword into the sagging flank of the beast. A torrent of curdled pus and viscera spewed forth from the puncture, followed by the scrabbling claws of parasitic Nurglings emerging from their host. Offalrott let out a thunderous chortle, stuffing the Nurglings back into his guts even as the rent in his side reknit. But before the wound sealed Ankhalas focused his mind to release a concentrated blast of furious energy. The psychic explosion erupted deep within Offalrott's belly, splitting his abdomen and sending bone and organ parts flying. The Daemon's laughing face twisted with blinding pain and rage. He tried to grab the Grey Knight with his claws and prehensile tongue, but Ankhalas was too fast. With a slash, a follow-up strike and a finishing blow, the Brotherhood Champion shredded the last of Offalrott's essence. Before the remains hit the floor, Ankhalas was running for the airlock. As the Brotherhood Champion abandoned the crippled frigate, the ship buckled and writhed as the warp claimed it.

TERMINATOR SQUADS

Nothing speaks so clearly of the Grey Knights' status as an elite amongst elite as the famed Terminator Squads that form the heart of their armies. Most Space Marine Chapters, be they a fresh Founding or a fragment of the Legions of yore, can count themselves lucky to own perhaps a few score suits of Terminator armour with which to outfit their 1st Company. The Grey Knights, on the other hand, can muster enough Tactical Dreadnought armour to outfit almost their entire Chapter. Yet formidable though the armour is, the warrior within is far more remarkable. To pursue the endless war against the Daemons of Chaos takes more than a mere Space Marine; it takes a Grey Knight – an altogether more difficile warrior, who is as far above other Adeptus Astartes as the Adeptus Astartes are above the common run of Humanity.

On Titan, unlike on other Chapter Planets, there is no initial training as a Scout. There is only an unyielding and brutal regime whose success at turning raw recruits into the finest warriors in the galaxy has been honed over the course of centuries. Only a fraction of the youths who enter the fortress monastery as neophytes survive the gruelling trials set before them. Those who finally emerge do so armoured with a superhuman physique enhanced by warded bio-implants. From their earliest days as a battle-brother they possess an unyielding will, razor-sharp battle skills and an all-encompassing knowledge of daemonic lore and psychic sorcery. In short, from the moment a Grey Knight initiate's training is complete, he is to be counted amongst the mightiest of Space Marines – and his abilities will only improve once he is tested in battle.

Each fully trained recruit costs the Imperium dearly. Thousands of warriors who would have served other Chapters valiantly must perish to find a single worthy of becoming a Grey Knight Terminator. However, this cost must be borne, for only those whose purity of spirit, strength and willpower has been proven can withstand the horrors the Chapter must face.

A Terminator's primary armament is a Nemesis force weapon of some kind, selected from the Chapter's armoury according to the skills and preferences of its wielder. As there is no doctrinal restriction on the types of weapons carried, it is rare for two Terminator Squads to bear exactly the same weapons combination – the Grey Knights have always favoured brutal efficiency over organisational mandate. Some prefer the crushing force of a Nemesis Daemon hammer, others the flurry of attacks granted by a matched pair of Nemesis falchions. Complementing this fearsome close quarter armament, each Terminator will also carry a storm bolter mounted upon his vambrace, thus leaving his hands free for a double-handed grip on his force weapon, or to access the supply of grenades belted at his waist.

Terminator Squads rarely operate a standard line of battle, for it seems that the Grey Knights are ever outnumbered by the baying foe. Thus, they must concentrate their attacks, picking their targets for full effect. As a result, Terminators often choose to teleport straight into the heart of battle, the better to catch the foe unawares in a storm of firepower and vengeful blades. Indeed, sometimes the only warning that a beset enemy will receive is the momentary flash of light and scent of ozone that precedes a teleport beam – by which time it is much too late.

THE LIBER DAEMONICA

Every Grey Knight carries a copy of the Liber Daemonica in a ceramite case on his breastplate. These gnarled tomes contain the Chapter's rites of battle, the prayers of sanctity and details of the traditional duties every Grey Knight must fulfil, from recruit to Supreme Grand Master.

The Liber Daemonica is an enduring symbol of the Grey Knight's devotion to his mission, and contains the cardinal tenets of lore culled from the dark knowledge caged within the Sanctum Sanctorum's walls. The books themselves are also potent talismans in their own right, with pages illuminated in silver and bound to a spine carved from the thigh bone of a martyred saint.

STRIKE SQUADS

It is said that amongst the greatest of military virtues is to be in the right place at the right time, and for no one is this truer than for the Grey Knights. Aided by the premonitions of their Prognosticars, the Grey Knights can often predict when and where a daemonic incursion will occur, and are sometimes in orbit or even planetside at the time of the invasion. Yet for the daemonic threat to be contained, each warp portal must either be sealed, destroyed or prevented from ever coming into being. For such tasks the Grey Knights rapidly teleport their Battle Brothers directly onto the target.

Strike Squads often form the vanguard of a Grey Knights' strike force. Equipped with lighter armour than the main battle line Terminator Squads, these warriors strike swiftly and surely, and are able to slip through gaps in the enemy line. At the onset of battle, a Grey Knight commander will invariably task one or more Strike Squads with the capture of vital locations and key objectives, deploying the Strike Squads via fixed teleporter to ensure the rapid seizure of isolated or inaccessible locations. Should aetheric disruption or sorcerous interference render such a teleport assault impossible, the Strike Squad will instead be deployed in Rhino or Razorback transports. With their lighter armour, Strike Squad warriors can fit into these cramped vehicles, where those clad in Tactical Dreadnought plate cannot.

Once in place, a Strike Squad can lay down a punishing stream of storm bolter and psycannon fire in support of the Chapter's main assault. These warriors are used to fighting alone, as they are frequently cut off from their kin until reinforcements arrive and a beachhead is established. Even unsupported and deep behind enemy lines, Strike Squads are far from easy targets. Once dug in, they are extremely difficult to dislodge – working in tight coordination, and armed with the devastating weaponry of Titan's armouries and their own formidable psychic abilities, they often prove to be a costly thorn in an enemy force's side.

Strike Squads are essential to the Grey Knights' way of war, for without their reconnaissance and battlefield preparation the Chapter's mass Terminator-led assaults would be a sledgehammer swung blindly in the darkness. When the full force of the Grey Knights' fury is finally deployed, the Strike Squads will emerge from their defensive positions and engage the foe, striking along the flank of the main assault to divert and disrupt any enemy counter-attacks. Harried, wrong-footed and dazed by these surgical strikes, the foe is left reeling, perfectly positioned for the killing stroke.

NEMESIS FORCE WEAPONS

Like the Grey Knights themselves, Nemesis weapons are a deadly fusion of advanced technology and the arcane. Crafted in iron and silver in the fortress monastery on Titan, these prized implements of warfare are inset with ancient runes and power field generators which cause them to crackle with eldritch energy.

'There are no walls we cannot breach, no havens where the foul spawn of the warp can cower, safe from our fury. Where'er evil resides, we shall seek it out, and deliver unto it the Emperor's Justice.'

- Interceptor Gallius Tharon, 2nd Brotherhood

INTERCEPTOR SQUADS

Interceptor Squads carry personal teleporters – backpack-sized devices that allow the squad to teleport site-to-site, without the massive arrays of machinery employed by conventional devices. Grey Knights equipped with personal teleporters can react to battlefield circumstances on the fly and cover huge straight-line distances by 'shunting' themselves through warp space.

Of all the warriors in service to the Imperium, only Grey Knights could hope to utilise such technology. The wearer must possess great fortitude of mind and body to traverse warp space without the protection of a Geller field. Worse, he must do so without the added protections of Terminator armour. Such wargear is too bulky for the limitations of the personal teleporter, which is why Interceptor Squads must, first and foremost, look to their own mental wards to act as defence against the untold and endless dangers of the warp.

Only the Grey Knights' inherent psychic ability and inviolate souls prevent them from suffering a truly horrific fate. The danger of personal teleportation is outweighed by the tactical opportunities afforded by its application. Interceptors can respond almost immediately to any changes in the enemy's tactics. With a single psychic communication, a beleaguered formation of Grey Knights can call for a squad of Interceptors to lend them aid, instantly turning the tide of battle in their favour. Crackling back into realspace from their warp-jaunt, these assault troops launch themselves into the astonished enemy, cleaving limbs and heads with mighty strokes from their Nemesis force weapons, and blasting into the thick of the foe with fusillades of bolter fire. As suddenly as they arrive, they disappear, leaving nothing but a faint aetheric static and the ruptured corpses of slaughtered Daemons in their wake.

As they are so often deployed as the tip of the spear, the 2nd Brotherhood maintains a large complement of Interceptor Squads, utilising them alongside warriors of the Strike Squads to unsettle and disorder the foe before the main assault. There are few defences that Interceptors cannot breach or bypass, and fewer foes prepared to deal with their disorienting attacks.

PSI WEAPONRY

Psilencers and psycannons are amongst the rarest armaments in the Imperium. Every one of these weapons is a prized relic dating back to the Dark Age of Technology, and as such is a sacred artefact of the Grey Knights Chapter. Both psilencers and psycannons are triggered by the wielder sending a jolt of psychic energy into the weapon's containment core. The payload released is a focused beam of force that shreds physical matter and saturates the air with burning psychic resonance.

PURGATION SQUADS

Purgation Squads are the Grey Knights' foremost means of delivering punishing firepower. Each squad carries not one, but up to four of the Chapter's heavy weapons.

In aspect, a Purgation Squad appears little different to the Devastator Squads employed by more conventional Space Marine Chapters. In doctrine, however, the two are markedly different. In most Chapters, duty in a Devastator Squad is seen as an excellent opportunity for a new recruit to experience the sights and sounds of a battlefield. Not so in the Grey Knights. The weaponry wielded by a Purgation Squad is twice as deadly, a hundred times rarer and ten thousand times more valuable than the more commonplace armaments carried by Space Marine Devastators. Therefore the members of a Purgation Squad must, if anything, have displayed an ability and resolve beyond that of their peers. Furthermore, whilst Devastators will normally advance behind the main assault, seeking out suitable locations from which to unleash covering fire, Purgation Squads are ever required to keep pace with the main attack, all the while picking out suitable targets for their weaponry.

The Grey Knights well appreciate that precision fire support can swing the fortunes of war, and so a battle-brother who earns a place in a Purgation Squad will not only have shown his steadfastness, but will also have proven himself to be the master of a keen eye and a steady hand. Yet sometimes a keen eye is not enough. Fate often ensures that the Grey Knights go to battle greatly outnumbered, and warriors outnumbered are prone to being overwhelmed whilst their attention is elsewhere. Those battle-brothers who serve in a Purgation Squad often hone their minds to see through the roiling energies of the warp, to perceive the foe and guide their shots upon him, regardless of what might lie in between. This astral vision allows a Purgation Squad to attempt seemingly impossible shots, bending the path of projectiles and even energy beams around obstacles mid-flight. Many an enemy has met a swift and bloody end whilst believing himself shielded by a rockcrete wall or the burnt-out hull of a tank. So it is that Purgation Squads are commonly seen as the truest expression of the Emperor's Will, for their onslaught cannot be stayed by earthly protections.

Once his duties are established, it is rare for a member of a Purgation Squad to see service elsewhere in the Chapter. A ranged battle stance, once mastered, is not easily set aside for blade upon blade tactics – indeed, those Grand Masters and Brother-Captains who once served in Purgation Squads are easily identified, as they continue to wield a psycannon or psilencer – the weapon that long ago became as much a part of their being as their own right arm. Those officers who do eventually set aside their heavy weapon for a storm bolter can be ranked amongst the finest shots in the Imperium, for the skill of a Purgator is one that never truly fades.

INCINERATORS

A body immolated can carry no corruption. As such, many Grey Knights revere the incinerator as the Chapter's most important tool of cleansing. An incinerator is a bright light in a galaxy filled with darkness, whose pilot flame is lit from fires carried forth from the Emperor's palace.

TECHMARINES

Techmarines are warrior-smiths of the highest calibre, responsible for the creation and repair of all the equipment employed by the Grey Knights. By their toil are suits of armour made ready for war, starships girded for interstellar voyages, Dreadnoughts awakened from slumber and Nemesis force weapons painstakingly crafted from silver and iron.

To begin his tutelage, a Techmarine-nominate takes a transport to Mars. Bearing silvered seals of introduction, he passes through the Ring of Iron and deep into the hidden forge cities of the Red Planet. Here he is immersed in the ancient and jealously guarded lore of the Adeptus Mechanicus. He learns to master the tools of the Techmarine, which will allow him to visit miracles upon sundered technology. Few are the harms that a Techmarine cannot make hale; he can fix minor weapon malfunctions with but a deft touch and, given time and appropriate facilities, bring wrecked and ruined battle tanks back to life.

Once he returns to Titan, a Techmarine is forever apart from his battle-brothers, for long years of training on Mars inculcate an entirely new set of traditions and rituals upon him. Few of these doctrines are entirely compatible with those of the Grey Knights. In fact, many stand in direct contradiction to the aims and goals of the Chapter. So it is that a Techmarine is called upon to balance these two opposed sides of his nature on a daily basis: to serve the goals and ideals of his Chapter, but according to the traditions of the Adeptus Mechanicus. Thus, though they are held in the greatest respect by their fellow warriors, Grey Knight Techmarines are typically a solemn and distant breed, finding greater comfort in the observance of their strange ceremonies and machine rites than in forging bonds of fellowship in the duelling chambers.

Adding to the inherent tension between their dual loyalties, Techmarines of the Grey Knights are expected to modify the weaponry and armoured vehicles that the Chapter utilises to better suit the Grey Knights' unique brand of warfare. Though the canticles of the Omnissiah forbid the alteration of blessed artefacts such as the Land Raider or the Stormraven Gunship, the unavoidable truth is that these vehicles require the correct preparation before they can enter the hellish battlefields upon which the Grey Knights fight their secret war. Modifications such as warded silver plating, psi-charged circuitry and Aegis shielding are installed in ritual ceremonies that last for many days, during which the Techmarine must appease the chosen machine spirit with ceaseless prayer and recitation. Though they find such unsanctioned modification distasteful, the Techmarines of the Grey Knights are well aware of the dire consequences of letting the foul touch of corruption wrest its way into the workings of one of the Chapter's war machines.

Much of the Techmarine's work is carried out in the foundries and workshops on Titan, yet he is no stranger to battle. Such is the Techmarine's skill that he can effect all but the most difficult of repairs amidst the howling furies of battle. Hunched alone beside a wounded machine, his mind concentrated on the task at hand, a Techmarine could appear to be easy prey, save for the array of cutters, welders and servo-arms at his command. Though primarily intended for repair, these tools can annihilate attackers just as easily…

SERVITORS

Techmarines are assisted in their duties by a retinue of Servitors, mind-scoured cyborgs equipped with an array of industrial tools and heavy weapons. These gruesome retainers were once mortals. Many of those in the Grey Knights' service fought in the armies of the Astra Militarum, until they were unfortunate enough to find themselves battling alongside the Grey Knights against some appalling empyrean incursion. Corruption cannot be risked, and so even those who survive such a hellish experience and emerge apparently mentally and physically intact cannot escape the clutches of the Inquisition. Most are simply executed en masse, though some are granted the honour of continuing to serve the Emperor, albeit in a lobotomised state of catatonia. The Grey Knights do not see this practice as morbid or distasteful. In their living death, Servitors continue the eternal struggle against the Dark Gods and their foul minions, far beyond the point at which a mortal soul would lose itself to madness or corruption.

Servitors are often employed on menial tasks, aiding Techmarines in the restoration of damaged vehicles and weapons, yet they are entirely capable of engaging the enemy should the need arise. In the fire and fury of combat, a Techmarine's Servitors can provide a blistering hail of covering fire as their master goes about his work, and turn their razor-edged sawblades and industrial laser cutters to hideously effective use upon those enemies foolish enough to draw near.

TRANSPORT VEHICLES

Though the Grey Knights often teleport into the thick of combat, many battles range over long distances where a single concentration of battle-brothers will not suffice. It is for this reason that the forges of Deimos produce powerful armoured transport vehicles, so that none on the plains of war may escape the Grey Knights' blades.

RHINOS

The Rhino armoured transport is one of the most venerated vehicles in service to the Imperium. Its origins lie in the murky mists of time, from when Man first reached out his hand to the stars and began the long process of colonisation.

Little has changed in the Rhino's design since those halcyon days, for its optimal balance of transport capacity, armour plating and battlefield manoeuvrability has been judged unassailably perfect by the Adeptus Mechanicus. It is small surprise therefore that the Rhino once served as the mainstay transport of all Mankind's armies. Alas, in these dark days, when many secrets of the Rhino's construction have been lost, and countless thousands of the vehicles have fallen into disrepair, only Space Marine Chapters, such as the Grey Knights, can muster a sufficient number of battle-ready Rhinos to suit their needs.

Chief amongst the Rhino's vaunted features is its array of automatic repair circuits. Originally intended to keep an unmaintained vehicle operational on an under-supplied colony world, these systems have long since proven their worth on the battlefields of Mankind's eternal war. So it is that a Rhino can sustain crippling damage to its tracks and engines, yet still return to full function without requiring outside attention. Those systems that the Rhino cannot mend for itself are likewise straightforward and intuitive to repair, allowing those initiated in the Machine God's mysteries to make major overhauls in a comparatively short span of time.

Rhinos in the Grey Knights' armoury are further modified by the Techmarines of the Chapter. Beneath the outer plating is a mesh-work of purified silver that conducts the psychic energy of the Grey Knight driver, as well as any battle-brothers that are being transported. Though this lattice does not cause the machine spirit to emit its own psychic force, it does project the Aegis of the Grey Knights within to surround the entire vehicle. Further additions are made to individual Rhinos. Some have recesses carved into their hull to ensconce vials of blessed oils, and others have a casing fitted to the driving panel to house the Liber Daemonica.

While still an important and honoured part of the Grey Knights' arsenal, the Rhino is a far less common sight here than in other Space Marine Chapters. This is nothing to do with combat doctrine or reliability, for the Rhino was ever a versatile and durable tank. Rather, this absence is due entirely to how the vehicle's physical limitations interact with the Chapter's favoured wargear. The Rhino's transport compartment is simply not large enough to accommodate Terminators and, as a great many Grey Knights go to war clad in Terminator armour, this clearly imposes limitations on the Rhino's usefulness to the Chapter. Nonetheless, the Rhino remains a highly valued transport for some of the Grey Knights' specialist troops. Purgation and Purifier Squads make particular use of Rhinos when on the advance, in order to reach optimum engagement range more swiftly, often advancing in the shadow of a Land Raider or with aerial supporting fire supplied by a Stormtalon Gunship.

RAZORBACKS

The Razorback is a heavily-armed variant of the Rhino troop transport that sacrifices some transport capacity for turret-mounted armaments. With the addition of recoil dampening servos and targeting augurs to the Rhino chassis, a Razorback can be equipped with everything from a twin heavy bolter to lascannons. The machine spirits of some Razorbacks in the Chapter's armoury have become perfectly attuned to a particular load-out, whereas other more bellicose machine spirits will awaken for war regardless of the weapons they bear.

Due to their versatility, Razorbacks are the perfect vehicles for small, elite squads of Grey Knights who need to move rapidly across the battlefield and require a mobile base of heavy fire support. The Rapiers Brotherhood are particularly fond of deploying Razorbacks with their strike forces, as oftentimes the bulkier Land Raiders are too ponderous to allow for the deft feints and daring flanking manoeuvres employed by these battle-brothers.

NEMESIS DREADKNIGHTS

It is a truth reluctantly acknowledged by the Grey Knights that valour, purity of spirit and battle-skill can only carry a warrior so far in single combat with a Greater Daemon of Chaos. After all, such diabolic monstrosities tower over even Terminators, and even the weakest wield the raw might of more than a dozen Space Marines. Yet it is often necessary that such hellspawn be faced down and destroyed, not by an entire brotherhood of Grey Knights, nor a score of Terminators, nor even a squad of Purifiers, but by a single valiant hero of the Chapter. For such desperate times was the Nemesis Dreadknight forged.

A Nemesis Dreadknight is a marvel of technology. At its indomitable heart is an adamantium-alloy skeleton, whose great limbs are given life by a compact but powerful plasma reactor. Over this are layered a series of bonded-ceramite plates and armoured control linkages.

Once a Grey Knight is strapped into the command harness on the Dreadknight's front, synaptic implants give him complete control of the machine's limbs and weapon systems – essentially granting him a surrogate body far mightier and more durable than his own. When matched with the Nemesis Dreadknight's devastating weapon systems and the all but impenetrable force field that protects the otherwise exposed pilot, this combination serves to elevate the Grey Knight's combat abilities to a point where he can withstand the blows of even the mightiest Greater Daemon, and unleash a fearsome counter-attack in reply.

It is unclear whether the technology that drives the Nemesis Dreadknight is a fragment of Mankind's lost knowledge, preserved through the Dark Age of Technology and the terrible times since, or if its origins owe more to alien influence. Either way, the Grey Knights hold their peace, and seem determined never to share their secrets. Few organisations in the Imperium could afford such an attitude, for it would bring them four-square into conflict with the edicts of the Adeptus Mechanicus, and indeed the principles under which all of Mankind's military is supplied. However, the Grey Knights answer only to the Inquisition, and so stand apart from such politics.

It would doubtless suit the Grey Knights to have every battle-brother take to the field aboard a Nemesis Dreadknight. Alas, not all Grey Knights have the strength of mind and subtlety of reaction required to master the exoskeleton's many combat stances. Only a very few battle-brothers show enough aptitude to begin the training, let alone be deemed fit to control such a weapon in the heat of battle. If the pilot is unable to devote enough of their psychic energy to manoeuvring the war machine it will remain stoically inert, for to rouse the powerful machine spirit that inhabits a Dreadknight requires an enormous feat of willpower. Even then, a battle-brother must also reserve a portion of their mind in order to maintain their Aegis, for they will be little good in combat if they leave themselves susceptible to the enemy. On the other hand, if the pilot directs even slightly too much psychic force to the articular servos, the colossal limbs of the Dreadknight may wrench violently and suddenly, tearing the Grey Knight's own limbs free from his torso. This is to say nothing of the control required to wield a Nemesis greatweapon, to deliver earth-shattering blows to the monsters of Chaos and slice through the plated hides of towering Greater Daemons.

So it is that Nemesis Dreadknight pilots are amongst the Grey Knights' most honoured warriors, for through long years of training and meditation they have mastered skills that are the envy of their brethren. Whilst other warriors would perhaps shirk such a brutal and exacting path, the battle-brothers of the Grey Knights embrace it, knowing that each trial furnishes them with new knowledge and skills.

KNIGHTLY LORDS

To become a Grand Master of the Grey Knights is a rare honour, and one that only the strongest-willed of warriors earn. It is no surprise that many such lordly heroes possess the mental fortitude required to enter battle clad in the raiment of the Nemesis Dreadknight. Deep within the Grey Knights' fastness on Titan lies the Hall of Giants, an echoing cloister lined with candle-lit alcoves. Within these loom ancient and revered Dreadknight suits, reserved for the use of the Chapter's Grand Masters. Whether teleporting into battle at the head of an elite strike force, striding out to duel the greatest Daemon lords, or embarking upon some doom-laden personal quest, when Grand Masters combine their exceptional might with that of the Nemesis Dreadknight, no malefic entity can stand against them.

DREADNOUGHTS

There are some battles that cannot be won by the valour of mortal men alone. Some conflicts are so terrible, and must be pursued in the face of such overwhelming odds, that victory can only be seized through the united might of the Chapter's greatest heroes. In such dark times, the Grey Knights descend to the Chamber of Heroes within the Sanctum Sanctorum and awaken the Chapter's Dreadnoughts.

There are few more awesome sights than a Dreadnought in full fury. More than twice the height of a man it stands, armed with the most fearsome weaponry the Grey Knights can provide, its furnace roaring with the joy of battle, and the earth cracking under its iron steps. As the Dreadnought advances, enemies scatter before it, their fire ricocheting off its adamantium hide.

Yet it is not the Dreadnought's armour, nor its Aegis reinforcement, nor even its armament, that make it such a deadly foe. That honour goes to the warrior that guides the goliath; a warrior long ago brought close to death by grievous wounds, and who must now forever dwell in the Dreadnought's cyborganic sarcophagus. Only the mightiest of the fallen are interred within a Dreadnought. To fight a Dreadnought, then, is to fight no mere machine, nor merely a great hero of the Chapter. It is to attempt nothing less than the defeat of a great warrior whose mortal frailties have long been set aside for a mechanical form as untiring and unyielding as his own will.

Such is a Dreadnought's wealth of combat experience that, once fully awakened, it can adopt any role required by the battle at hand, from long-range fire support to spearheading assaults. Indeed, amongst the Grey Knights, it is far from unusual for a Dreadnought to serve as a secondary commander, holding authority over the main strike force, thus allowing the Brother-Captain to direct efforts elsewhere. This should come as no surprise, for many Dreadnought pilots attained the rank of Brother-Captain, or even Grand Master, before their internment, and relish the opportunity to apply their strategic acumen to fresh campaigns. Those battle-brothers fighting under the gaze of these Venerable Dreadnoughts are sure to redouble their efforts. To take to the battlefield alongside such a warrior is to walk in the shadow of an undying legend and, in such company, a battle-brother will not be found wanting.

Venerable Dreadnoughts house ancient warriors whose sheer belligerence is testament to the Grey Knights' hatred of their foe. Refusing to release their grip on mortal existence until the last Daemon has been driven from the galaxy and the last warp rift has been finally sealed, these honoured battle-brothers can shrug off even catastrophic damage, ignoring enemy blows and incoming shots as if they were a mere annoyance.

It might seem strange that Dreadnoughts are awoken at only the direst times. Yet the Grand Masters of the Grey Knights know that to depend too heavily upon these ancient heroes is to dishonour the gift of their service – for these battle-brothers have already died once for their Chapter. And so, when the dark times have passed, the Dreadnoughts return to the Chamber of Heroes, there to slumber in the darkness, dreaming of battles yet to come…

LAND RAIDERS

More than a simple transport, a Land Raider is an engine of unstoppable destruction. These behemoths carry enough weaponry to obliterate several ranks of enemies, even before their deadly payload of waiting Grey Knights is disgorged. The sheer bulk and durability of a Land Raider makes it a linchpin in many strike forces.

Unlike much of the Imperium, the Grey Knights do not make extensive use of armoured tanks. Theirs is a more personal war, fought with both feet planted firmly on the ground, and won with a warrior's own weapons and fortitude. That the Land Raider has been granted a permanent place in the Chapter's armouries is testimony to the high regard in which it is held by the Grand Masters of Titan. Unlike most other vehicles employed by the Grey Knights, each Land Raider has a robust and thriving machine spirit, capable of operating any of the tank's many weapon systems, or even taking command of the drive mechanisms. For this reason, the Chapter's Techmarines hold the Land Raider to be amongst the most blessed of the Omnissiah's works.

Superficially, a Grey Knight Land Raider appears identical to those employed the galaxy over. It has the same bonded ceramite and adamantium hull, sealed-environment transport chamber and forbidding weaponry. Yet beneath the adamantium hull lies the wealth of modifications that are required to transform the Land Raider into an integral part of the Chapter's weaponry. Bundles of psi-charged circuitry, psycho-reactive armour plates and charged sigils allow the Land Raider's crew to not only control their tank through psychic prompting, but also effect battlefield repairs simply by focusing their mental might. Aegis components, adapted from those found in Grey Knight armour, are threaded throughout the vehicle and offer a measure of protection against enemy psykers.

Such modifications are carried out on Titan at the hands of the Chapter's Techmarines – a sacred duty that is performed with religious precision. These modifications are technically a breach of the Adeptus Mechanicus' hidebound protocols, and serve both as an example of the unusual status that the Grey Knights enjoy, and as a reminder that there are some technologies that even the Adeptus Mechanicus is forbidden to touch. Nonetheless, each of these adaptations is necessary for the vehicle to survive the raging warp-sorceries and corrupted weaponry of the Grey Knights' hated foes.

LAND RAIDER CRUSADERS

The Crusader is a variant of the core Land Raider design, purpose-built to smash its way through the enemy's forward line with a storm of hurricane bolter fire before disgorging its occupants directly into their midst. The removal of the Land Raider's typical godhammer lascannon armament – along with their bulky power generators – grants the Crusader improved transport capacity, perfect for the Grey Knights who so often enter battle clad in heavy Terminator plate.

One of the Swordbearers favoured tactics when tasked with overrunning a fortified position is to simply batter their way through with several Land Raider Crusaders. As the smoke and debris clears, access hatches drop open and silver figures stride forth through the devastation, swords raised high and storm bolters spitting a punishing barrage of consecrated metal.

LAND RAIDER REDEEMERS

The Land Raider Redeemer is designed to dominate the brutal grind of urban warfare. When a hive city falls to heretical cultists, or a forge world is overrun by a daemonic invasion, the hallowed Land Raider Redeemers are brought forth from the Grey Knights armoury.

Two huge flamestorm cannons are mounted on each side of the vehicle, ready to spew a super-heated inferno that can melt through thick armour and hide as if they were wax. Before each battle, Grey Knight Techmarines ritually blend sacred oils and unguents into the promethium fuel of these vicious weapons, creating a blessed concoction of liquid flame that sticks to Daemon flesh hungrily, devouring the creature's physical form in a few swift yet agonising moments.

Like the Crusader-pattern Land Raiders, Redeemers are armed with frag assault launchers to shred nearby enemies with blasted shrapnel as the Grey Knights within charge into combat.

GUNSHIPS

The gunships of the Grey Knights streak over the battlefield like bolts of silver lightning, striking enemy battle lines on the ground and leaving little in their wake but purified flesh and scorched debris. Once a strike force of battle-brothers has been teleported to dispatch the survivors, the gunships soar towards the clouds to continue to unleash their rain of destruction.

STORMRAVEN GUNSHIPS

Stormraven Gunships are close support strike aircraft and transport ships, and the Grey Knight's deployment method of choice when teleportation cannot be employed. Amongst the 2nd Brotherhood they are often known as the Ravens of Deliverance. A Stormraven transport compartment can accommodate no less than six Terminator-armoured Grey Knights, or twice as many battle-brothers in less-bulky power armour. Such a troop complement is impressive by itself but, should further firepower be required, the Stormraven can also carry a Dreadnought in its rear grapples. Being swifter and more agile than the Chapter's Thunderhawk Gunships, the Stormraven allows for a more reliable battlefield insertion – particularly when the skies are screaming with daemonic turbulence, as they so often are when the Grey Knights are on campaign.

The Stormraven Gunship has been in the Grey Knights' service for millennia. It is perhaps the most versatile weapon in their armoury, able to perform fire support, interdiction and armoured assault missions according to the needs of the battle at hand. It is often likened to a flying Land Raider, for the two craft have many similarities, not least of which is a sophisticated machine spirit capable of operating the craft's weapon systems with all the accuracy and deftness of the crew. However, the Stormraven outguns even the legendary Land Raider – it is nothing less than a flying fortress.

STORMTALON GUNSHIPS

Equipped with vectored afterburners which grant them astonishing manoeuvrability, Stormtalon Gunships provide the Grey Knights with a devastating ground attack option. Screaming out of warp-wracked skies in tight formation, the Chapter's Stormtalons strafe their prey with pinpoint volleys of cannon and bolter fire, each sanctified round finding its home in Daemonic flesh or hell-forged metal. Swift and deadly, these aircraft are perfectly suited to the precision assaults in which the Grey Knights specialise. The Chapter has further adapted the aircraft for their purposes with the addition of advanced psycho-neural interfaces that grant the pilot an almost symbiotic connection with the Gunship's machine spirit. Grey Knight Techmarines fly their Stormtalons with a preternatural awareness and skill, weaving and jinking through cascades of searing warpfire and swarms of leather-winged horrors.

While the Chapter often deploys them as the Codex Astartes advises – as heavily armed escorts for the bulkier Stormraven transports – Grey Knight Stormtalons also see use as vanguard assault craft, where their adaptability and firepower render them invaluable. Even a single such vessel, operating in psychic consort with a strike force of battle-brothers, can cut a bloody swathe through a Daemonic warhost, allowing its brethren free reign to strike at the heart of the foe. Though they specialise in the destruction of ground targets, Stormtalons are also adept at air-to-air combat, able to burn winged Daemon Engines from the sky with a salvo of consecrated warheads.

STORMHAWK INTERCEPTORS

The secret history of the Grey Knights is replete with tales of duels fought between noble champions and soul-hungering monsters from the depths of the empyrean. Often these legendary contests were fought with blade and claw, yet no small number took place in the roiling skies above a battlefield, where lightning-fast Stormhawk Interceptors engaged warp-spawned drakes in death-defying displays of aeronautical skill. Stormhawks are peerless dogfighting craft – sleek, swift and bristling with weaponry, including the devastating forward las-talon that can punch through even the thickest daemonic flesh-metal, and the Icarus stormcannon whose gyro-scrying arrays lock on to the swiftest winged monstrosities. To the Techmarines of the Grey Knights they are noble and redoubtable steeds, their restless machine spirits ever eager to take to the skies in search of fresh abominations to slay.

The Grey Knights maintain several attack wings of Stormhawks, whose task it is to clear the stratosphere ahead of full-scale ground deployment. The intrepid Deliverers – ever at the forefront of the Grey Knights' holy crusade – finds particular use for these vessels, counting amongst its number such renowned squadrons as the Spear of Titan and the Andaemus Flight.

THE 666TH CHAPTER

The Grey Knights have a long and proud history in the service of the Emperor. They bear the icons and colours of their Chapter with honour. When arrayed for battle there are few sights as inspiring as a Grey Knights brotherhood.

Lord Kaldor Draigo, Supreme Grand Master

Grand Master Voldus

Grey Knight

Grey Knight Justicar

Grey Knight with psycannon

Standing together like a shining silver shield as their airborne brothers command the skies, a strike force of Grey Knights clashes with the frothing hordes of Khorne. As the battle lines draw closer, the warriors incant the true names of their enemies and prepare to drive their daemonic foes screaming from the battlefield and back into the warp.

Deploying by teleport strike into the heart of a daemonic incursion, a squad of Paladins stands defiant atop a rocky outcropping. Though vastly outnumbered, their psychic might and spiritual purity evens the battle, allowing them to withstand wave after wave of attacks as they ready their banishment rituals.

Paladin Ancient with Brotherhood Banner

Brother-Captain Stern

Paladin

Paladin with incinerator

Paladin with Nemesis falchions

Apothecary

Terminator Justicar

Terminator with Nemesis Daemon hammer

Terminator with psilencer

Clad in gleaming Terminator armour, the heroes of the Grey Knights lead a devastating assault into a capering horde of Tzeentchian Daemons. Backed by looming Dreadknights and a mighty Land Raider, they carve an ichor-spattered path through their foes.

Converted Librarian with Nemesis warding stave

Converted Brother-Captain

These Grey Knights warriors have been built using characters from the Space Marines range of Citadel Miniatures. Using components from the Grey Knights Terminators kit, they have been given the markings, armour and wargear of their Chapter. Some have been fitted with Grey Knights pauldrons that bear their personal heraldry and record their achievements. The Librarian also carries a Nemesis warding stave, and his left gauntlet has been swapped for one bearing a wrist-mounted storm bolter.

Converted Chaplain

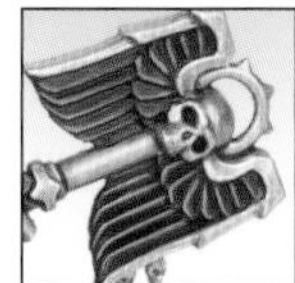

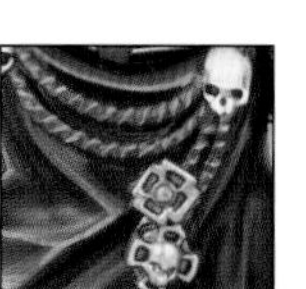

Venerable Dreadnought

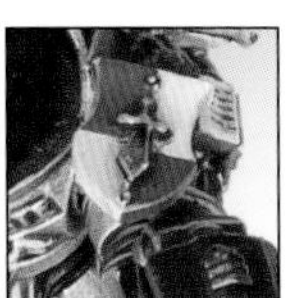

Brotherhood Champion

WARHAMMER TV

If you would like to learn more about building, converting and painting your Citadel Miniatures, you can visit our dedicated YouTube channel Warhammer TV, where you can watch regular videos on every aspect of the Warhammer hobby. This includes advice on how to paint your models to the highest standards, featuring the insider knowledge of expert miniature painters. Visit youtube.com/WarhammerTV to get involved!

Venerable Dreadnought Brother Moritar leads his Grey Knights brethren into battle, his twin lascannon spitting bolts of energy fit to banish even the greatest Daemons, and his power fist ready to crush the unrighteous.

Purifier with Nemesis warding stave

Purifier with Nemesis Daemon hammer

Purifier with Nemesis falchions

Knight of the Flame

Interceptors with Nemesis force swords

Interceptor with incinerator

Interceptor Justicar with Nemesis Daemon hammer

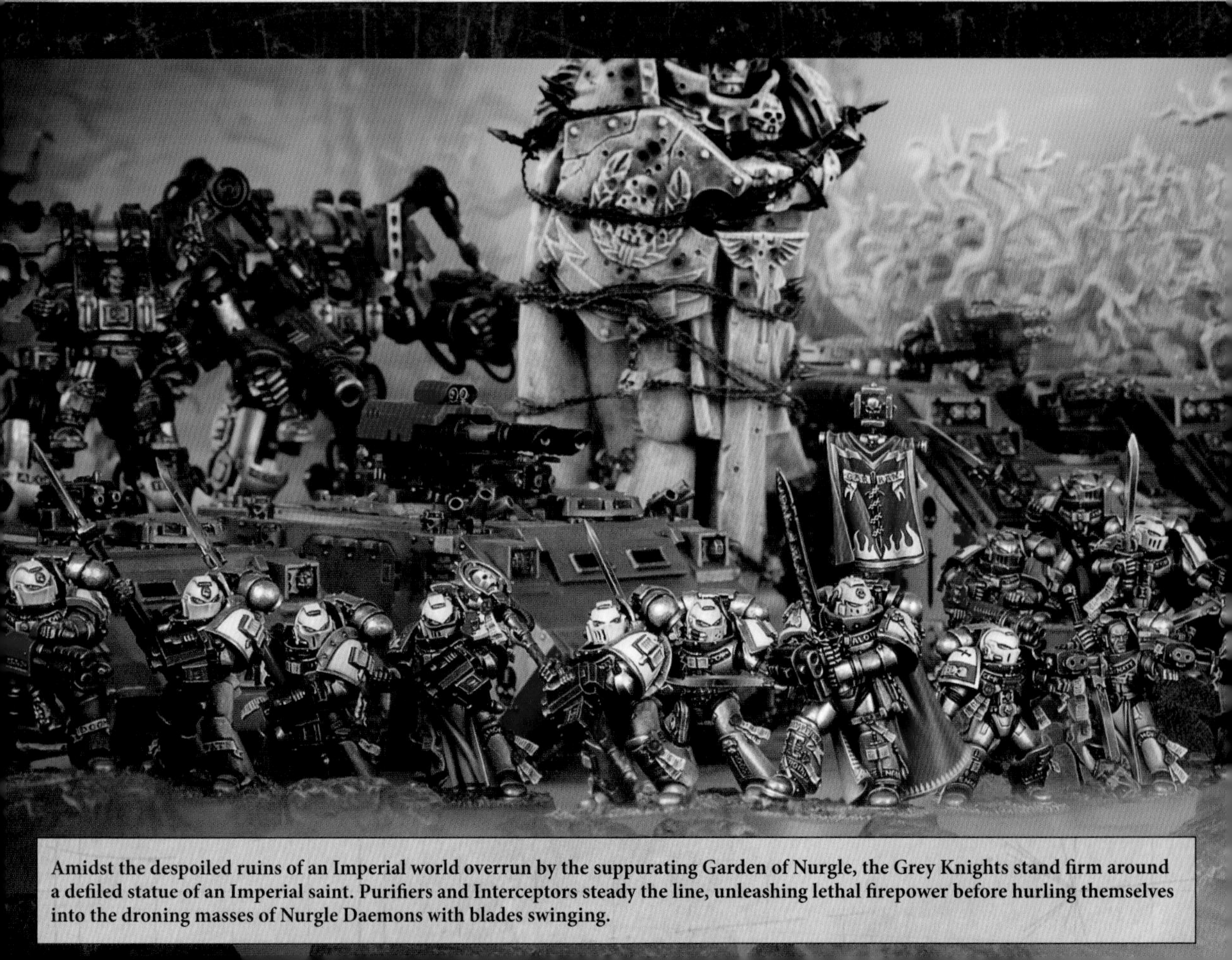

Amidst the despoiled ruins of an Imperial world overrun by the suppurating Garden of Nurgle, the Grey Knights stand firm around a defiled statue of an Imperial saint. Purifiers and Interceptors steady the line, unleashing lethal firepower before hurling themselves into the droning masses of Nurgle Daemons with blades swinging.

Forge World

The ornate doors and turret gunner on this Land Raider Crusader are from Forge World, who produce finely detailed resin models and components that are compatible with Citadel Miniatures. They can be found at forgeworld.co.uk.

Land Raider Crusader with Forge World door accessories and gunner

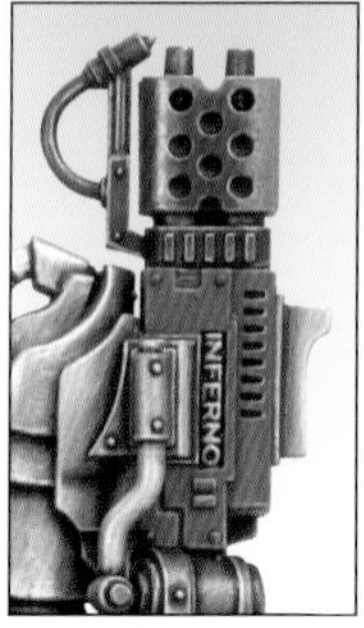

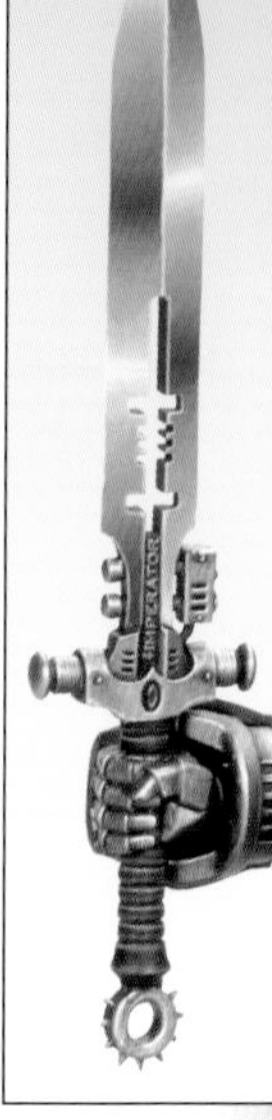

Nemesis Dreadknight

Faced with deadly threats both on the ground and in the air, Grey Knight brotherhoods often call upon the aerial support and withering firepower of Stormtalon Gunships and Stormhawk Interceptors.

BAND OF HEROES

A strike force of Grey Knights is an elite fighting force that possesses a phenomenal amount of killing power despite its limited numbers. This starting force was chosen to exemplify the specialist nature of these formidable warriors.

When collecting a Warhammer 40,000 army, it is always helpful to come up with a rough idea of how you want your collection to look, feel and behave on the tabletop. This might be a broad, sweeping narrative, an optimised combination of units and rules, or perhaps just a starting concept to build on.

The collection featured here draws inspiration from the story of the Grey Knights as the perpetually outnumbered but never outgunned elites of the Imperium, and features some of the most potent units the army has available.

The force is led by a Librarian, a powerful psyker even by Grey Knights standards who can harness the power of the warp to deal out damage or protect his allies. The core of the force is a Terminator Squad, its warriors so potent that they would be considered elite specialists in most other armies. Providing support is a looming Nemesis Dreadknight, a powerful fusion of warrior and war engine.

As this force comprises one HQ unit, one Troops unit and one Heavy Support unit, it meets the requirements of a Patrol Detachment as described in the *Warhammer 40,000* rulebook. This band of heroes is therefore Battle-forged, ensuring they have access to three Command Points to spend on Stratagems. Additionally, with every model being a beautifully detailed individual hero, they present an enjoyable painting and modelling challenge and will make for an impressive-looking force on the tabletop.

Librarian Nematon leads Squad Arkas and Nemesis Dreadknight Brother Denathos into battle.

GATHER THE BROTHERHOOD!

Librarian Nematon and his brothers can form the core of a Grey Knights army, but they are just the start. Great heroes, elite warriors, powerful war machines and hurtling aircraft will all join the muster, the better to slay the Emperor's greatest foes.

Above can be seen a sizeable Grey Knights army, representing the sort of versatile and impressive collection that many players set out to assemble. Built around the initial models in the Band of Heroes collection on the previous page, this is the sort of army that could be hurled into day-long epic Warhammer 40,000 battles and emerge, bloodied but victorious!

This army is an elite Daemon-fighting force, designed to swiftly target the most significant enemy threat and withstand anything it might throw at them. As such, every infantry model included is clad in Terminator armour, providing them with enhanced protection and teleport technology.

Terminator Squad Torvul joins Squad Arkas, along with two squads of Paladins – Squads Gerontin and Rolthus. A veritable company of heroes leads these warriors. Alongside Librarian Nematon is Apothecary Aralan and two Paladin Ancients – Brothers Elius and Vorian – each wielding a sacred banner. Chaplain Kamander safeguards the spiritual purity of his brothers, while at the force's head strides Brother-Captain Markhus, his Nemesis force sword at the ready. These last two models are conversions built around the Space Marine Terminator Chaplain and Terminator Captain models. Spare shoulder pads and other components have been used to create these distinctive heroes, taken from leftover parts of the Paladin kits.

No Warhammer 40,000 army is complete without an array of death-dealing war machines ready to blow the enemy to bits. As such, Nemesis Dreadknight Brother Denathos has been joined by a second of these mighty walkers, brother Pentakhar.

Another armoured combat walker supports the force in the form of Venerable Dreadnought Brother Moritar, whose twin lascannon makes him a formidable threat to any war engines or rampaging monsters that the enemy may deploy. Even more firepower is brought to the force, along with heavily armoured troop-transport capacity, by the Land Raider *Blade of Titan* and the Land Raider Crusader *Fortress of Purity.*

To round off the force, which now consists of two Patrol Detachments and a larger Vanguard Detachment, the Stormhawk Interceptor *Litany of Purgation* provides fast-moving air support and is the bane of flying enemy units.

1. **Brother-Captain Markhus**
2. **Librarian Nematon**
3. **Chaplain Kamander**
4. **Paladin Ancient Elius**
5. **Paladin Ancient Vorian**
6. **Apothecary Aralan**
7. **Terminator Squad Arkas**
8. **Terminator Squad Torvul**
9. **Paladin Squad Gerontin**
10. **Paladin Squad Rolthus**
11. **Nemesis Dreadknights Denathos and Pentakhar**
12. **Venerable Dreadnought Moritar**
13. **Land Raider *Blade of Titan***
14. **Land Raider Crusader *Fortress of Purity***
15. **Stormhawk Interceptor *Litany of Purgation***

THE ARMY OF TITAN

This section contains all of the datasheets that you will need to fight battles with your Grey Knights miniatures, and the rules for all of the weapons they can wield in battle. Each datasheet includes the characteristics profiles of the unit it describes, as well as any wargear and special abilities it may have. Any abilities that are common to several units are described below and referenced on the datasheets themselves.

And They Shall Know No Fear

Every Grey Knight has been subjected to an intensive regime of hypno-indoctrination and spiritual fortification, so that they may stand unafraid before the horrors of the warp.

You can re-roll failed Morale tests for this unit.

Daemon Hunters

Grey Knights are implacable foes of all things daemonic, their doctrines and weapons honed to the slaughter of warpspawn.

If this unit attacks any Daemons in the Fight phase, you can re-roll failed wound rolls for those attacks.

Rites of Banishment

Employing ancient tomes and reams of arcane lore, the Grey Knights perform sacred rituals that sever the bonds holding Daemons to the material plane, banishing them to the roiling hellscape from whence they came.

When this unit manifests the *Smite* psychic power, it has a range of 12" rather than 18", and the target unit suffers only 1 mortal wound rather than D3 (whether or not the result of the Psychic test is more than 10) – unless the target unit is a Daemon, in which case it suffers 3 mortal wounds instead of D3.

'We are the warriors of the Grey Knights, armoured in Faith, shielded by Devotion and armed with Purity of Purpose. But greater even than these, we carry the light of the divine Emperor of Man into the dark places to purge the Daemonic wherever it may be found.'

- Brother-Captain Arvann Stern

Teleport Strike

Teleportation assaults are a favoured tactic of the Grey Knights. The Chapter's commanders have mastered this aggressive form of war, and the ancient technology upon which it relies.

During deployment, you can set up this unit in a teleportarium chamber instead of placing it on the battlefield. At the end of any of your Movement phases this unit can teleport into battle – set it up anywhere on the battlefield that is more than 9" away from any enemy models.

GREY KNIGHTS WARGEAR LISTS

Many of the units you will find on the following pages reference one or more of the following wargear lists (e.g. Melee Weapons). When this is the case, the unit may take any item from the appropriate list below. The profiles for the weapons in these lists can be found in the Armoury of Titan section (pg 92).

MELEE WEAPONS

- Nemesis Daemon hammer
- Nemesis force halberd
- Nemesis force sword
- Nemesis warding stave
- Two Nemesis falchions*

*May not be taken by an Apothecary.

SPECIAL WEAPONS

- Incinerator
- Psilencer
- Psycannon

DREADNOUGHT HEAVY WEAPONS

- Multi-melta
- Heavy plasma cannon
- Twin lascannon

COMBI-WEAPONS

- Combi-flamer
- Combi-melta
- Combi-plasma

12 POWER

Lord Kaldor Draigo

NAME	M	WS	BS	S	T	W	A	Ld	Sv
Lord Kaldor Draigo	5"	2+	2+	4	4	7	5	9	2+

Lord Kaldor Draigo is a single model armed with the Titansword, a storm shield, a storm bolter, frag grenades, krak grenades and psyk-out grenades. Only one of this model may be included in your army.

WEAPON	RANGE	TYPE	S	AP	D	ABILITIES
Storm bolter	24"	Rapid Fire 2	4	0	1	-
The Titansword	Melee	Melee	+4	-4	3	-
Frag grenade	6"	Grenade D6	3	0	1	-
Krak grenade	6"	Grenade 1	6	-1	D3	-
Psyk-out grenade	6"	Grenade D3	2	0	1	Each time you roll a hit roll of 6+ for this weapon when targeting a **PSYKER** or **DAEMON**, the target suffers a mortal wound instead of the normal damage.

ABILITIES

And They Shall Know No Fear, Daemon Hunters, Rites of Banishment (pg 62)

Bane of Evil: When a friendly **GREY KNIGHTS** unit within 6" of Lord Kaldor Draigo makes an attack against a **DAEMON** unit in the Fight phase, you can re-roll damage rolls for that unit.

Storm Shield: Lord Kaldor Draigo has a 3+ invulnerable save.

Chapter Master: You can re-roll failed hit rolls for friendly **GREY KNIGHTS** units that are within 6" of Lord Kaldor Draigo.

Warp Emergence: During deployment, you can set up Lord Kaldor Draigo in the warp instead of placing him on the battlefield. At the end of any of your Movement phases Lord Kaldor Draigo can emerge from the warp – set him up anywhere on the battlefield that is more than 9" away from any enemy models.

PSYKER

Lord Kaldor Draigo can attempt to manifest two psychic powers in each friendly Psychic phase, and attempt to deny two psychic powers in each enemy Psychic phase. He knows the *Smite* psychic power and two psychic powers from the Sanctic discipline (pg 101).

FACTION KEYWORDS: IMPERIUM, ADEPTUS ASTARTES, GREY KNIGHTS

KEYWORDS: CHARACTER, INFANTRY, GRAND MASTER, TERMINATOR, PSYKER, LORD KALDOR DRAIGO

'I shall defend Mankind to my last breath, even should the Realm of Chaos be emptied and its entire host arrayed against me. If the Dark Gods themselves walked this world, still would I raise my sword and bar their way. As a Grey Knight, I can do no less.'

- Lord Kaldor Draigo

Draigo strides out of the warp to deliver the fury of his Chapter to the slavering throngs of Daemons.

10 POWER

Grand Master Voldus

NAME	M	WS	BS	S	T	W	A	Ld	Sv
Grand Master Voldus	5"	2+	2+	4	4	6	5	9	2+

Grand Master Voldus is a single model armed with Malleus Argyrum, a storm bolter, frag grenades, krak grenades and psyk-out grenades. Only one of this model may be included in your army.

WEAPON	RANGE	TYPE	S	AP	D	ABILITIES
Storm bolter	24"	Rapid Fire 2	4	0	1	-
Malleus Argyrum	Melee	Melee	x2	-3	3	-
Frag grenade	6"	Grenade D6	3	0	1	-
Krak grenade	6"	Grenade 1	6	-1	D3	-
Psyk-out grenade	6"	Grenade D3	2	0	1	Each time you roll a hit roll of 6+ for this weapon when targeting a **Psyker** or **Daemon**, the target suffers a mortal wound instead of the normal damage.

ABILITIES

And They Shall Know No Fear, Daemon Hunters, Rites of Banishment, Teleport Strike (pg 62-63)

Iron Halo: Grand Master Voldus has a 4+ invulnerable save.

Rites of Battle: You can re-roll hit rolls of 1 for friendly **Grey Knights** units within 6" of Grand Master Voldus.

PSYKER

Grand Master Voldus can attempt to manifest three psychic powers in each friendly Psychic phase, and attempt to deny three psychic powers in each enemy Psychic phase. He knows the *Smite* psychic power and three psychic powers from the Sanctic discipline (pg 101).

FACTION KEYWORDS Imperium, Adeptus Astartes, Grey Knights

KEYWORDS Character, Infantry, Grand Master, Terminator, Psyker, Voldus

10 POWER

Grand Master

NAME	M	WS	BS	S	T	W	A	Ld	Sv
Grand Master	5"	2+	2+	4	4	6	5	9	2+

A Grand Master is a single model armed with a Nemesis force halberd, storm bolter, frag grenades, krak grenades and psyk-out grenades.

WEAPON	RANGE	TYPE	S	AP	D	ABILITIES
Storm bolter	24"	Rapid Fire 2	4	0	1	-
Nemesis force halberd	Melee	Melee	+1	-2	D3	-
Frag grenade	6"	Grenade D6	3	0	1	-
Krak grenade	6"	Grenade 1	6	-1	D3	-
Psyk-out grenade	6"	Grenade D3	2	0	1	Each time you roll a hit roll of 6+ for this weapon when targeting a **Psyker** or **Daemon**, the target suffers a mortal wound instead of the normal damage.

WARGEAR OPTIONS

- This model may replace his Nemesis force halberd with an item from the *Melee Weapons* list.
- This model may replace his storm bolter with an item from the *Special Weapons* list.

ABILITIES

And They Shall Know No Fear, Daemon Hunters, Rites of Banishment, Teleport Strike (pg 62-63)

Iron Halo: This model has a 4+ invulnerable save.

Rites of Battle: You can re-roll hit rolls of 1 for friendly **Grey Knights** units within 6" of this model.

PSYKER

This model can attempt to manifest two psychic powers in each friendly Psychic phase, and attempt to deny one psychic power in each enemy Psychic phase. It knows the *Smite* psychic power and one psychic power from the Sanctic discipline (pg 101).

FACTION KEYWORDS Imperium, Adeptus Astartes, Grey Knights

KEYWORDS Character, Infantry, Terminator, Psyker, Grand Master

14 POWER

Grand Master
in Nemesis Dreadknight

NAME	M	WS	BS	S	T	W	A	Ld	Sv
Grand Master in Nemesis Dreadknight	*	2+	*	6	6	12	*	9	2+

DAMAGE
Some of this model's characteristics change as it suffers damage, as shown below:

REMAINING W	M	BS	A
7-12+	8"	2+	5
4-6	7"	3+	4
1-3	6"	4+	3

A Grand Master in Nemesis Dreadknight is a single model armed with two dreadfists.

WEAPON	RANGE	TYPE	S	AP	D	ABILITIES
Gatling psilencer	24"	Heavy 12	4	0	D3	-
Heavy incinerator	12"	Heavy D6	6	-1	2	This weapon automatically hits its target.
Heavy psycannon	24"	Heavy 6	7	-1	2	-
Dreadfist	Melee	Melee	x2	-3	D3	If a model is equipped with two dreadfists, each time it fights it can make 1 additional attack with them.
Nemesis Daemon greathammer	Melee	Melee	x2	-4	D6	When a model attacks with this weapon, you must subtract 1 from the hit roll. Damage rolls of less than 3 count as 3 for this weapon.
Nemesis greatsword	Melee	Melee	+4	-3	D6	-

WARGEAR OPTIONS

- This model may take up to two different weapons from the following:
  - Heavy incinerator
  - Gatling psilencer
  - Heavy psycannon
- This model may replace one of its dreadfists with a Nemesis Daemon greathammer or a Nemesis greatsword.
- This model may take a Dreadknight teleporter.

ABILITIES

And They Shall Know No Fear, Daemon Hunters, Rites of Banishment (pg 62)

Force Shielding and Iron Halo: This model has a 4+ invulnerable save.

Rites of Battle: You can re-roll hit rolls of 1 for friendly GREY KNIGHTS units within 6" of this model.

Dreadknight Teleporter: If this model has a Dreadknight teleporter, then during deployment, you can set it up in a teleportarium chamber instead of placing it on the battlefield. At the end of any of your Movement phases this model can teleport into battle – set it up anywhere on the battlefield that is more than 9" away from any enemy models.

PSYKER

This model can attempt to manifest two psychic powers in each friendly Psychic phase, and attempt to deny one psychic power in each enemy Psychic phase. It knows the *Smite* psychic power and one psychic power from the Sanctic discipline (pg 101).

FACTION KEYWORDS

IMPERIUM, ADEPTUS ASTARTES, GREY KNIGHTS

KEYWORDS

CHARACTER, VEHICLE, NEMESIS DREADKNIGHT, PSYKER, GRAND MASTER

Castellan Crowe

7 Power

NAME	M	WS	BS	S	T	W	A	Ld	Sv
Castellan Crowe	6"	2+	2+	4	4	5	5	8	2+

Castellan Crowe is a single model armed with the Black Blade of Antwyr, a storm bolter, frag grenades, krak grenades and psyk-out grenades. Only one of this model may be included in your army.

WEAPON	RANGE	TYPE	S	AP	D	ABILITIES
Storm bolter	24"	Rapid Fire 2	4	0	1	-
The Black Blade of Antwyr	Melee	Melee	User	0	1	-
Frag grenade	6"	Grenade D6	3	0	1	-
Krak grenade	6"	Grenade 1	6	-1	D3	-
Psyk-out grenade	6"	Grenade D3	2	0	1	Each time you roll a hit roll of 6+ for this weapon when targeting a PSYKER or DAEMON, the target suffers a mortal wound instead of the normal damage.

ABILITIES

And They Shall Know No Fear, Daemon Hunters (pg 62)

Heroic Sacrifice: If Castellan Crowe is slain in the Fight phase, he can immediately pile in and attack before being removed as a casualty.

Purifying Flame: When Castellan Crowe manifests the *Smite* psychic power, it only has a range of 3", but it inflicts D6 mortal wounds instead of D3 (whether or not the result of the Psychic test is more than 10).

Iron Halo: Castellan Crowe has a 4+ invulnerable save.

Master Swordsman: You can re-roll failed hit and wound rolls for Castellan Crowe in the Fight phase. In addition, each time you make a successful wound roll for Castellan Crowe in the Fight phase, you can immediately make another attack with the Black Blade of Antwyr, though these additional attacks cannot generate any further attacks.

PSYKER

Castellan Crowe can attempt to manifest two psychic powers in each friendly Psychic phase, and attempt to deny one psychic power in each enemy Psychic phase. He knows the *Smite* psychic power and one psychic power from the Sanctic discipline (pg 101).

FACTION KEYWORDS

IMPERIUM, ADEPTUS ASTARTES, GREY KNIGHTS

KEYWORDS

CHARACTER, INFANTRY, BROTHERHOOD CHAMPION, PSYKER, CASTELLAN CROWE

Castellan Crowe is possessed of a powerful will. A lesser soul would have been corrupted by the Black Blade of Antwyr long ago.

Brother-Captain Stern exemplifies the valour and resolve of the Grey Knights, fighting on defiantly despite the curse that afflicts him.

8 POWER

BROTHER-CAPTAIN STERN

NAME	M	WS	BS	S	T	W	A	Ld	Sv
Brother-Captain Stern	5"	2+	2+	4	4	6	4	9	2+

Brother-Captain Stern is a single model armed with a Nemesis force sword, storm bolter, frag grenades, krak grenades and psyk-out grenades. Only one of this model may be included in your army.

WEAPON	RANGE	TYPE	S	AP	D	ABILITIES
Storm bolter	24"	Rapid Fire 2	4	0	1	-
Nemesis force sword	Melee	Melee	User	-3	D3	-
Frag grenade	6"	Grenade D6	3	0	1	-
Krak grenade	6"	Grenade 1	6	-1	D3	-
Psyk-out grenade	6"	Grenade D3	2	0	1	Each time you roll a hit roll of 6+ for this weapon when targeting a PSYKER or DAEMON, the target suffers a mortal wound instead of the normal damage.

ABILITIES

And They Shall Know No Fear, Daemon Hunters, Teleport Strike (pg 62-63)

The Strands of Fate: In each of your turns, you can choose to re-roll a single failed hit or wound roll, or a single failed saving throw for Brother-Captain Stern. However, if you do so, your opponent can re-roll a single failed hit or wound roll, or a single failed saving throw for one of their models in their next turn.

Iron Halo: Brother-Captain Stern has a 4+ invulnerable save.

Psychic Locus: When a friendly GREY KNIGHTS unit within 6" of any BROTHER-CAPTAINS manifests the *Smite* power, double its range.

Zone of Banishment: When Brother-Captain Stern manifests the *Smite* psychic power, it has a range of 6" rather than 18". Additionally, the target unit suffers only 1 mortal wound rather than D3 (whether or not the result of the Psychic test is more than 10) – unless the target is a DAEMON, in which case it suffers 3 mortal wounds instead of D3 – and all DAEMON units within 6" of Brother-Captain Stern suffer 1 mortal wound.

PSYKER

Brother-Captain Stern can attempt to manifest two psychic powers in each friendly Psychic phase, and attempt to deny one psychic power in each enemy Psychic phase. He knows the *Smite* psychic power and one psychic power from the Sanctic discipline (pg 101).

FACTION KEYWORDS

IMPERIUM, ADEPTUS ASTARTES, GREY KNIGHTS

KEYWORDS

CHARACTER, INFANTRY, BROTHER-CAPTAIN, TERMINATOR, PSYKER, STERN

Brother-Captain

NAME	M	WS	BS	S	T	W	A	Ld	Sv
Brother-Captain	5"	2+	2+	4	4	6	4	9	2+

A Brother-Captain is a single model armed with a Nemesis force halberd, storm bolter, frag grenades, krak grenades and psyk-out grenades.

WEAPON	RANGE	TYPE	S	AP	D	ABILITIES
Storm bolter	24"	Rapid Fire 2	4	0	1	-
Nemesis force halberd	Melee	Melee	+1	-2	D3	-
Frag grenade	6"	Grenade D6	3	0	1	-
Krak grenade	6"	Grenade 1	6	-1	D3	-
Psyk-out grenade	6"	Grenade D3	2	0	1	Each time you roll a hit roll of 6+ for this weapon when targeting a **PSYKER** or **DAEMON**, the target suffers a mortal wound instead of the normal damage.

WARGEAR OPTIONS	• This model may replace his Nemesis force halberd with an item from the *Melee Weapons* list. • This model may replace his storm bolter with an item from the *Special Weapons* list.
ABILITIES	**And They Shall Know No Fear, Daemon Hunters, Rites of Banishment, Teleport Strike** (pg 62-63) **Iron Halo:** This model has a 4+ invulnerable save. **Psychic Locus:** When a friendly **GREY KNIGHTS** unit within 6" of any **BROTHER-CAPTAINS** manifests the *Smite* power, double its range.
PSYKER	This model can attempt to manifest one psychic power in each friendly Psychic phase, and attempt to deny one psychic power in each enemy Psychic phase. It knows the *Smite* psychic power and one psychic power from the Sanctic discipline (pg 101).
FACTION KEYWORDS	**IMPERIUM, ADEPTUS ASTARTES, GREY KNIGHTS**
KEYWORDS	**CHARACTER, INFANTRY, TERMINATOR, PSYKER, BROTHER-CAPTAIN**

Brother-Captains are amongst the Chapter's deadliest warriors, inspiring leaders whose place is at the very heart of the battle line.

Librarian

NAME	M	WS	BS	S	T	W	A	Ld	Sv
Librarian	5"	2+	2+	4	4	5	3	9	2+

A Librarian is a single model armed with a Nemesis warding stave, frag grenades, krak grenades and psyk-out grenades.

WEAPON	RANGE	TYPE	S	AP	D	ABILITIES
Storm bolter	24"	Rapid Fire 2	4	0	1	-
Nemesis warding stave	Melee	Melee	+2	-1	D3	A model armed with this weapon has a 5+ invulnerable save against attacks made in the Fight phase. If it already has an invulnerable save, add 1 to invulnerable saving throws you make for it in the Fight phase instead.
Frag grenade	6"	Grenade D6	3	0	1	-
Krak grenade	6"	Grenade 1	6	-1	D3	-
Psyk-out grenade	6"	Grenade D3	2	0	1	Each time you roll a hit roll of 6+ for this weapon when targeting a **Psyker** or **Daemon**, the target suffers a mortal wound instead of the normal damage.

WARGEAR OPTIONS	• This model may replace his Nemesis warding stave with an item from the *Melee Weapons* list. • This model may take a storm bolter or an item from the *Combi-weapons* list.
ABILITIES	**And They Shall Know No Fear, Daemon Hunters, Rites of Banishment, Teleport Strike** (pg 62-63) **Crux Terminatus:** This model has a 5+ invulnerable save. **Psychic Hood:** You can add 1 to Deny the Witch tests you take for this model against enemy **Psykers** within 12".
PSYKER	This model can attempt to manifest two psychic powers in each friendly Psychic phase, and attempt to deny two psychic powers in each enemy Psychic phase. It knows the *Smite* psychic power and two psychic powers from the Sanctic discipline (pg 101).
FACTION KEYWORDS	**Imperium, Adeptus Astartes, Grey Knights**
KEYWORDS	**Character, Infantry, Terminator, Psyker, Librarian**

Grey Knights Librarians are the mightiest and most strong-willed psykers in a Chapter filled with psychically gifted battle-brothers.

Servants of both Titan and Mars, Grey Knights Techmarines maintain and repair the Chapter's sacred war machines.

7 POWER

Techmarine

NAME	M	WS	BS	S	T	W	A	Ld	Sv
Techmarine	6"	3+	2+	4	4	4	3	8	2+

A Techmarine is a single model armed with a power axe, two servo-arms, a boltgun, a plasma cutter, a flamer, frag grenades, krak grenades and psyk-out grenades.

WEAPON	RANGE	TYPE	S	AP	D	ABILITIES
Bolt pistol	12"	Pistol 1	4	0	1	-
Boltgun	24"	Rapid Fire 1	4	0	1	-
Flamer	8"	Assault D6	4	0	1	This weapon automatically hits its target.
Plasma cutter	When attacking with this weapon, choose one of the profiles below.					
- Standard	12"	Assault 1	7	-3	1	-
- Supercharge	12"	Assault 1	8	-3	2	On a hit roll of 1, the bearer is slain after all of this weapon's shots have been resolved.
Power axe	Melee	Melee	+1	-2	1	-
Servo-arm	Melee	Melee	x2	-2	3	Each servo-arm can only be used to make one attack each time this model fights. When a model attacks with this weapon, you must subtract 1 from the hit roll.
Frag grenade	6"	Grenade D6	3	0	1	-
Krak grenade	6"	Grenade 1	6	-1	D3	-
Psyk-out grenade	6"	Grenade D3	2	0	1	Each time you roll a hit roll of 6+ for this weapon when targeting a **Psyker** or **Daemon**, the target suffers a mortal wound instead of the normal damage.

WARGEAR OPTIONS	• This model may replace its boltgun with a bolt pistol.
ABILITIES	**And They Shall Know No Fear, Daemon Hunters, Rites of Banishment** (pg 62) **Blessing of the Omnissiah:** At the end of your Movement phase, this model can repair a single friendly **Grey Knights Vehicle** (other than models that can **Fly**) within 1". That vehicle regains D3 wounds lost earlier in the battle. A vehicle can only be repaired once each turn.
PSYKER	This model can attempt to manifest one psychic power in each friendly Psychic phase, and attempt to deny one psychic power in each enemy Psychic phase. It knows the *Smite* psychic power and one psychic power from the Sanctic discipline (pg 101).
FACTION KEYWORDS	**Imperium, Adeptus Astartes, Grey Knights**
KEYWORDS	**Character, Infantry, Psyker, Techmarine**

8 POWER — CHAPLAIN

NAME	M	WS	BS	S	T	W	A	Ld	Sv
Chaplain	5"	2+	2+	4	4	5	3	9	2+

A Chaplain is a single model armed with a crozius arcanum, storm bolter, frag grenades, krak grenades and psyk-out grenades.

WEAPON	RANGE	TYPE	S	AP	D	ABILITIES
Storm bolter	24"	Rapid Fire 2	4	0	1	-
Crozius arcanum	Melee	Melee	+1	-1	2	-
Frag grenade	6"	Grenade D6	3	0	1	-
Krak grenade	6"	Grenade 1	6	-1	D3	-
Psyk-out grenade	6"	Grenade D3	2	0	1	Each time you roll a hit roll of 6+ for this weapon when targeting a PSYKER or DAEMON, the target suffers a mortal wound instead of the normal damage.

ABILITIES

And They Shall Know No Fear, Daemon Hunters, Rites of Banishment, Teleport Strike (pg 62-63)

Litanies of Hate: You can re-roll failed hit rolls in the Fight phase for friendly GREY KNIGHTS units within 6" of this model.

Rosarius: This model has a 4+ invulnerable save.

Spiritual Leaders: All friendly GREY KNIGHTS units within 6" of this model can use the Chaplain's Leadership instead of their own.

PSYKER

This model can attempt to manifest one psychic power in each friendly Psychic phase, and attempt to deny one psychic power in each enemy Psychic phase. It knows the *Smite* psychic power and one psychic power from the Sanctic discipline (pg 101).

FACTION KEYWORDS: IMPERIUM, ADEPTUS ASTARTES, GREY KNIGHTS

KEYWORDS: CHARACTER, INFANTRY, TERMINATOR, PSYKER, CHAPLAIN

6 POWER — BROTHERHOOD CHAMPION

NAME	M	WS	BS	S	T	W	A	Ld	Sv
Brotherhood Champion	6"	2+	2+	4	4	4	4	8	2+

A Brotherhood Champion is a single model armed with a Nemesis force sword, storm bolter, frag grenades, krak grenades and psyk-out grenades.

WEAPON	RANGE	TYPE	S	AP	D	ABILITIES
Storm bolter	24"	Rapid Fire 2	4	0	1	-
Nemesis force sword	Melee	Melee	User	-3	D3	-
Frag grenade	6"	Grenade D6	3	0	1	-
Krak grenade	6"	Grenade 1	6	-1	D3	-
Psyk-out grenade	6"	Grenade D3	2	0	1	Each time you roll a hit roll of 6+ for this weapon when targeting a PSYKER or DAEMON, the target suffers a mortal wound instead of the normal damage.

ABILITIES

And They Shall Know No Fear, Daemon Hunters, Rites of Banishment (pg 62)

Heroic Sacrifice: If this model is slain in the Fight phase, he can immediately pile in and attack before being removed as a casualty.

Iron Halo: This model has a 4+ invulnerable save.

The Perfect Warrior: At the start of each Fight phase, you must choose a combat stance for this model to adopt for the duration of that phase – either the Sword Strike stance or the Blade Shield stance. If you choose the Sword Strike stance, add 1 to this model's wound rolls for that phase. If you choose the Blade Shield stance, add 1 to this model's saving throws for that phase.

PSYKER

This model can attempt to manifest one psychic power in each friendly Psychic phase, and attempt to deny one psychic power in each enemy Psychic phase. It knows the *Smite* psychic power and one psychic power from the Sanctic discipline (pg 101).

FACTION KEYWORDS: IMPERIUM, ADEPTUS ASTARTES, GREY KNIGHTS

KEYWORDS: CHARACTER, INFANTRY, PSYKER, BROTHERHOOD CHAMPION

Wielding Nemesis weapons and clad in impenetrable plate, Grey Knights Terminators are a hammer blow aimed at the heart of the foe.

13 POWER

Terminator Squad

NAME	M	WS	BS	S	T	W	A	Ld	Sv
Grey Knight Terminator	5"	3+	3+	4	4	2	2	7	2+
Terminator Justicar	5"	3+	3+	4	4	2	3	8	2+

This unit contains 1 Terminator Justicar and 4 Grey Knight Terminators. It can include up to 5 additional Grey Knight Terminators (**Power Rating +13**). Each model is armed with a Nemesis force sword, storm bolter, frag grenades, krak grenades and psyk-out grenades.

WEAPON	RANGE	TYPE	S	AP	D	ABILITIES
Storm bolter	24"	Rapid Fire 2	4	0	1	-
Nemesis force sword	Melee	Melee	User	-3	D3	-
Frag grenade	6"	Grenade D6	3	0	1	-
Krak grenade	6"	Grenade 1	6	-1	D3	-
Psyk-out grenade	6"	Grenade D3	2	0	1	Each time you roll a hit roll of 6+ for this weapon when targeting a PSYKER or DAEMON, the target suffers a mortal wound instead of the normal damage.

WARGEAR OPTIONS

- Any model may replace his Nemesis force sword with an item from the *Melee Weapons* list.
- For every five models in the unit, one Grey Knight Terminator may replace his storm bolter with an item from the *Special Weapons* list.

ABILITIES

And They Shall Know No Fear, Daemon Hunters, Rites of Banishment, Teleport Strike (pg 62-63)

Crux Terminatus: All models in this unit have a 5+ invulnerable save.

Combat Squads: Before any models are deployed at the start of the game, a Terminator Squad containing 10 models may be split into two units, each containing 5 models.

PSYKER

This unit can attempt to manifest one psychic power in each friendly Psychic phase, and attempt to deny one psychic power in each enemy Psychic phase. It knows the *Smite* psychic power and one psychic power from the Sanctic discipline (pg 101).

When manifesting or denying a psychic power, first select a model in the unit – measure range, visibility, etc. from this model. If this unit suffers Perils of the Warp, it suffers D3 mortal wounds as described in the core rules, but units within 6" will only suffer damage if the Perils of the Warp cause the last model in the manifesting unit to be slain.

FACTION KEYWORDS IMPERIUM, ADEPTUS ASTARTES, GREY KNIGHTS

KEYWORDS INFANTRY, TERMINATOR, PSYKER, TERMINATOR SQUAD

Strike Squads are adaptable and deadly vanguard troops, whose forward reconnaissance is invaluable to Grey Knights battle plans.

7 POWER

Strike Squad

NAME	M	WS	BS	S	T	W	A	Ld	Sv
Grey Knight	6"	3+	3+	4	4	1	1	7	3+
Justicar	6"	3+	3+	4	4	1	2	8	3+

This unit contains 1 Justicar and 4 Grey Knights. It can include up to 5 additional Grey Knights (**Power Rating +7**). Each model is armed with a Nemesis force sword, storm bolter, frag grenades, krak grenades and psyk-out grenades.

WEAPON	RANGE	TYPE	S	AP	D	ABILITIES
Storm bolter	24"	Rapid Fire 2	4	0	1	-
Nemesis force sword	Melee	Melee	User	-3	D3	-
Frag grenade	6"	Grenade D6	3	0	1	-
Krak grenade	6"	Grenade 1	6	-1	D3	-
Psyk-out grenade	6"	Grenade D3	2	0	1	Each time you roll a hit roll of 6+ for this weapon when targeting a PSYKER or DAEMON, the target suffers a mortal wound instead of the normal damage.

WARGEAR OPTIONS

- Any model may replace his Nemesis force sword with an item from the *Melee Weapons* list.
- For every five models in the unit, one Grey Knight may replace his Nemesis force sword and storm bolter with an item from the *Special Weapons* list.

ABILITIES

And They Shall Know No Fear, Daemon Hunters, Rites of Banishment, Teleport Strike (pg 62-63)

Combat Squads: Before any models are deployed at the start of the game, a Strike Squad containing 10 models may be split into two units, each containing 5 models.

PSYKER

This unit can attempt to manifest one psychic power in each friendly Psychic phase, and attempt to deny one psychic power in each enemy Psychic phase. It knows the *Smite* psychic power and one psychic power from the Sanctic discipline (pg 101).

When manifesting or denying a psychic power, first select a model in the unit – measure range, visibility, etc. from this model. If this unit suffers Perils of the Warp, it suffers D3 mortal wounds as described in the core rules, but units within 6" will only suffer damage if the Perils of the Warp cause the last model in the manifesting unit to be slain.

FACTION KEYWORDS IMPERIUM, ADEPTUS ASTARTES, GREY KNIGHTS

KEYWORDS INFANTRY, PSYKER, STRIKE SQUAD

Apothecary

NAME	M	WS	BS	S	T	W	A	Ld	Sv
Apothecary	5"	2+	3+	4	4	5	4	8	2+

An Apothecary is a single model armed with a Nemesis force sword, frag grenades, krak grenades and psyk-out grenades.

WEAPON	RANGE	TYPE	S	AP	D	ABILITIES
Nemesis falchion	Melee	Melee	User	-2	D3	-
Nemesis force sword	Melee	Melee	User	-3	D3	-
Frag grenade	6"	Grenade D6	3	0	1	-
Krak grenade	6"	Grenade 1	6	-1	D3	-
Psyk-out grenade	6"	Grenade D3	2	0	1	Each time you roll a hit roll of 6+ for this weapon when targeting a **Psyker** or **Daemon**, the target suffers a mortal wound instead of the normal damage.

WARGEAR OPTIONS

- This model may replace its Nemesis force sword with a Nemesis falchion or an item from the *Melee Weapons* list.

ABILITIES

And They Shall Know No Fear, Daemon Hunters, Rites of Banishment, Teleport Strike (pg 62-63)

Crux Terminatus: This model has a 5+ invulnerable save.

Narthecium: At the end of any of your Movement phases, the Apothecary can attempt to heal or revive a single model. Select a friendly **Grey Knights Infantry** unit within 3" of the Apothecary. If that unit contains a wounded model, it immediately regains D3 lost wounds. If the chosen unit contains no wounded models but one or more of its models have been slain during the battle, roll a D6. On a 4+ a single slain model is returned to the unit with 1 wound remaining. If an Apothecary fails to revive a model in this manner he can do nothing else for the remainder of the turn (shoot, charge, fight etc.) as he recovers the gene-seed of the fallen warrior. A unit can only be the target of the Narthecium ability once in each turn.

PSYKER

This model can attempt to manifest one psychic power in each friendly Psychic phase, and attempt to deny one psychic power in each enemy Psychic phase. It knows the *Smite* psychic power and one psychic power from the Sanctic discipline (pg 101).

FACTION KEYWORDS

Imperium, Adeptus Astartes, Grey Knights

KEYWORDS

Character, Infantry, Terminator, Psyker, Apothecary

The medical expertise of an Apothecary is of incalculable value to the Grey Knights Chapter, whose numbers are all too few.

7 POWER

Brotherhood Ancient

NAME	M	WS	BS	S	T	W	A	Ld	Sv
Brotherhood Ancient	5"	3+	3+	4	4	5	3	8	2+

A Brotherhood Ancient is a single model armed with a storm bolter, frag grenades, krak grenades and psyk-out grenades.

WEAPON	RANGE	TYPE	S	AP	D	ABILITIES
Storm bolter	24"	Rapid Fire 2	4	0	1	-
Nemesis falchion	Melee	Melee	User	-2	D3	-
Frag grenade	6"	Grenade D6	3	0	1	-
Krak grenade	6"	Grenade 1	6	-1	D3	-
Psyk-out grenade	6"	Grenade D3	2	0	1	Each time you roll a hit roll of 6+ for this weapon when targeting a **Psyker** or **Daemon**, the target suffers a mortal wound instead of the normal damage.

WARGEAR OPTIONS
- This model may take a Nemesis falchion.

ABILITIES

And They Shall Know No Fear, Daemon Hunters, Rites of Banishment, Teleport Strike (pg 62-63)

Crux Terminatus: This model has a 5+ invulnerable save.

Sacred Banner: Friendly **Grey Knights** units within 6" of any sacred banners add 1 to their Leadership characteristic. In addition, models from friendly **Grey Knights Infantry** units that are within 6" of any sacred banners when they fight can make 1 additional attack that phase.

PSYKER

This model can attempt to manifest one psychic power in each friendly Psychic phase, and attempt to deny one psychic power in each enemy Psychic phase. It knows the *Smite* psychic power and one psychic power from the Sanctic discipline (pg 101).

FACTION KEYWORDS: **Imperium, Adeptus Astartes, Grey Knights**

KEYWORDS: **Character, Infantry, Ancient, Terminator, Psyker, Brotherhood Ancient**

One of the 1st Brotherhood's many banners, commemorating the Chapter's great victory on the Daemon world of Archaenologos.

Paladin Squad

10 Power

NAME	M	WS	BS	S	T	W	A	Ld	Sv
Paladin	5"	3+	3+	4	4	3	3	8	2+
Paragon	5"	2+	3+	4	4	3	3	9	2+

This unit contains 1 Paragon and 2 Paladins. It can include up to 2 additional Paladins (**Power Rating +9**), or up to 7 additional Paladins (**Power Rating +22**). Each model is armed with a Nemesis force sword, storm bolter, frag grenades, krak grenades and psyk-out grenades.

WEAPON	RANGE	TYPE	S	AP	D	ABILITIES
Storm bolter	24"	Rapid Fire 2	4	0	1	-
Nemesis force sword	Melee	Melee	User	-3	D3	-
Frag grenade	6"	Grenade D6	3	0	1	-
Krak grenade	6"	Grenade 1	6	-1	D3	-
Psyk-out grenade	6"	Grenade D3	2	0	1	Each time you roll a hit roll of 6+ for this weapon when targeting a PSYKER or DAEMON, the target suffers a mortal wound instead of the normal damage.

WARGEAR OPTIONS

- Any model may replace his Nemesis force sword with an item from the *Melee Weapons* list.
- For every five models in the unit, two Paladins may replace their storm bolter with an item from the *Special Weapons* list.

ABILITIES

And They Shall Know No Fear, Daemon Hunters, Rites of Banishment, Teleport Strike (pg 62-63)

Crux Terminatus: Models in this unit have a 5+ invulnerable save.

Combat Squads: Before any models are deployed at the start of the game, a Paladin Squad containing 10 models may be split into two units, each containing 5 models.

PSYKER

This unit can attempt to manifest one psychic power in each friendly Psychic phase, and attempt to deny one psychic power in each enemy Psychic phase. It knows the *Smite* psychic power and one psychic power from the Sanctic discipline (pg 101).

When manifesting or denying a psychic power, first select a model in the unit – measure range, visibility, etc. from this model. If this unit suffers Perils of the Warp, it suffers D3 mortal wounds as described in the core rules, but units within 6" will only suffer damage if the Perils of the Warp cause the last model in the manifesting unit to be slain.

FACTION KEYWORDS: IMPERIUM, ADEPTUS ASTARTES, GREY KNIGHTS

KEYWORDS: INFANTRY, PALADIN, TERMINATOR, PSYKER, PALADIN SQUAD

Paladin Ancients bear aloft their banners of honour, inspiring their fellow warriors to forge new legends of valour and heroism.

7 Power

Paladin Ancient

NAME	M	WS	BS	S	T	W	A	Ld	Sv
Paladin Ancient	5"	2+	3+	4	4	5	4	8	2+

A Paladin Ancient is a single model armed with a storm bolter, frag grenades, krak grenades and psyk-out grenades.

WEAPON	RANGE	TYPE	S	AP	D	ABILITIES
Storm bolter	24"	Rapid Fire 2	4	0	1	-
Nemesis falchion	Melee	Melee	User	-2	D3	-
Frag grenade	6"	Grenade D6	3	0	1	-
Krak grenade	6"	Grenade 1	6	-1	D3	-
Psyk-out grenade	6"	Grenade D3	2	0	1	Each time you roll a hit roll of 6+ for this weapon when targeting a PSYKER or DAEMON, the target suffers a mortal wound instead of the normal damage.

WARGEAR OPTIONS

- This model may take a Nemesis falchion or replace its storm bolter with an item from the *Special Weapons* list.

ABILITIES

And They Shall Know No Fear, Daemon Hunters, Rites of Banishment, Teleport Strike (pg 62-63)

Crux Terminatus: This model has a 5+ invulnerable save.

Sacred Banner: Friendly GREY KNIGHTS units within 6" of any sacred banners add 1 to their Leadership characteristic. In addition, models from friendly GREY KNIGHTS INFANTRY units that are within 6" of any sacred banners when they fight can make 1 additional attack that phase.

PSYKER

This model can attempt to manifest one psychic power in each friendly Psychic phase, and attempt to deny one psychic power in each enemy Psychic phase. It knows the *Smite* psychic power and one psychic power from the Sanctic discipline (pg 101).

FACTION KEYWORDS IMPERIUM, ADEPTUS ASTARTES, GREY KNIGHTS

KEYWORDS CHARACTER, INFANTRY, PALADIN, TERMINATOR, PSYKER, ANCIENT

9 POWER

Purifier Squad

NAME	M	WS	BS	S	T	W	A	Ld	Sv
Purifier	6"	3+	3+	4	4	1	1	8	3+
Knight of the Flame	6"	3+	3+	4	4	1	2	9	3+

This unit contains 1 Knight of the Flame and 4 Purifiers. It can include up to 5 additional Purifiers (**Power Rating +9**). Each model is armed with a Nemesis force sword, storm bolter, frag grenades, krak grenades and psyk-out grenades.

WEAPON	RANGE	TYPE	S	AP	D	ABILITIES
Storm bolter	24"	Rapid Fire 2	4	0	1	-
Nemesis force sword	Melee	Melee	User	-3	D3	-
Frag grenade	6"	Grenade D6	3	0	1	-
Krak grenade	6"	Grenade 1	6	-1	D3	-
Psyk-out grenade	6"	Grenade D3	2	0	1	Each time you roll a hit roll of 6+ for this weapon when targeting a **Psyker** or **Daemon**, the target suffers a mortal wound instead of the normal damage.

WARGEAR OPTIONS

- Any model may replace his Nemesis force sword with an item from the *Melee Weapons* list.
- For every five models in the unit, two Purifiers may replace their Nemesis force sword and storm bolter with an item from the *Special Weapons* list.

ABILITIES

And They Shall Know No Fear, Daemon Hunters (pg 62)

Purifying Flame: When this unit manifests the *Smite* psychic power, it only has a range of 3", but it inflicts D6 mortal wounds instead of D3 (whether or not the result of the Psychic test is more than 10).

Combat Squads: Before any models are deployed at the start of the game, a Purifier Squad containing 10 models may be split into two units, each containing 5 models.

PSYKER

This unit can attempt to manifest one psychic power in each friendly Psychic phase, and attempt to deny one psychic power in each enemy Psychic phase. It knows the *Smite* psychic power and one psychic power from the Sanctic discipline (pg 101).

When manifesting or denying a psychic power, first select a model in the unit – measure range, visibility, etc. from this model. If this unit suffers Perils of the Warp, it suffers D3 mortal wounds as described in the core rules, but units within 6" will only suffer damage if the Perils of the Warp cause the last model in the manifesting unit to be slain.

FACTION KEYWORDS: Imperium, Adeptus Astartes, Grey Knights

KEYWORDS: Infantry, Psyker, Purifier Squad

Given motion by the will of fallen champions, Dreadnoughts are walking tanks that bristle with fearsome weaponry.

8 POWER

Dreadnought

NAME	M	WS	BS	S	T	W	A	Ld	Sv
Dreadnought	6"	3+	3+	6	7	8	4	8	3+

A Dreadnought is a single model equipped with an assault cannon, a storm bolter and a Dreadnought combat weapon.

WEAPON	RANGE	TYPE	S	AP	D	ABILITIES
Assault cannon	24"	Heavy 6	6	-1	1	-
Heavy flamer	8"	Heavy D6	5	-1	1	This weapon automatically hits its target.
Missile launcher	When attacking with this weapon, choose one of the profiles below.					
- Frag missile	48"	Heavy D6	4	0	1	-
- Krak missile	48"	Heavy 1	8	-2	D6	-
Storm bolter	24"	Rapid Fire 2	4	0	1	-
Dreadnought combat weapon	Melee	Melee	x2	-3	3	-

WARGEAR OPTIONS

- This model may replace its assault cannon with an item from the *Dreadnought Heavy Weapons* list.
- This model may replace its Dreadnought combat weapon and storm bolter with a missile launcher.
- This model may replace its storm bolter with a heavy flamer.

ABILITIES

Daemon Hunters, Rites of Banishment (pg 62)

Explodes: If this model is reduced to 0 wounds, roll a D6 before removing the model from the battlefield; on a 6 it explodes, and each unit within 3" suffers D3 mortal wounds.

Smoke Launchers: Once per game, instead of shooting any weapons in the Shooting phase, this model can use its smoke launchers; until your next Shooting phase your opponent must subtract 1 from all hit rolls for ranged weapons that target this vehicle.

PSYKER

This model can attempt to manifest one psychic power in each friendly Psychic phase, and attempt to deny one psychic power in each enemy Psychic phase. It knows the *Smite* psychic power and one psychic power from the Sanctic discipline (pg 101).

FACTION KEYWORDS Imperium, Adeptus Astartes, Grey Knights

KEYWORDS Vehicle, Psyker, Dreadnought

9 Power — Venerable Dreadnought

NAME	M	WS	BS	S	T	W	A	Ld	Sv
Venerable Dreadnought	6"	2+	2+	6	7	8	4	8	3+

A Venerable Dreadnought is a single model equipped with an assault cannon, a storm bolter and a Dreadnought combat weapon.

WEAPON	RANGE	TYPE	S	AP	D	ABILITIES
Assault cannon	24"	Heavy 6	6	-1	1	-
Heavy flamer	8"	Heavy D6	5	-1	1	This weapon automatically hits its target.
Missile launcher	When attacking with this weapon, choose one of the profiles below.					
- Frag missile	48"	Heavy D6	4	0	1	-
- Krak missile	48"	Heavy 1	8	-2	D6	-
Storm bolter	24"	Rapid Fire 2	4	0	1	-
Dreadnought combat weapon	Melee	Melee	x2	-3	3	-

WARGEAR OPTIONS

- This model may replace its assault cannon with a weapon from the *Dreadnought Heavy Weapons* list.
- This model may replace its Dreadnought combat weapon and storm bolter with a missile launcher.
- This model may replace its storm bolter with a heavy flamer.

ABILITIES

Daemon Hunters, **Rites of Banishment** (pg 62)

Smoke Launchers: Once per game, instead of shooting any weapons in the Shooting phase, this model can use its smoke launchers; until your next Shooting phase your opponent must subtract 1 from all hit rolls for ranged weapons that target this vehicle.

Explodes: If this model is reduced to 0 wounds, roll a D6 before removing the model from the battlefield; on a 6 it explodes, and each unit within 3" suffers D3 mortal wounds.

Unyielding Ancient: Roll a D6 each time this model loses a wound; on a 6 the damage is ignored and that wound is not lost.

PSYKER

This model can attempt to manifest one psychic power in each friendly Psychic phase, and attempt to deny one psychic power in each enemy Psychic phase. It knows the *Smite* psychic power and one psychic power from the Sanctic discipline (pg 101).

FACTION KEYWORDS: Imperium, Adeptus Astartes, Grey Knights

KEYWORDS: Vehicle, Dreadnought, Psyker, Venerable Dreadnought

3 Power — Servitors

NAME	M	WS	BS	S	T	W	A	Ld	Sv
Servitor	5"	5+	5+	3	3	1	1	6	4+

This unit contains 4 Servitors. Each model is armed with a servo-arm.

WEAPON	RANGE	TYPE	S	AP	D	ABILITIES
Heavy bolter	36"	Heavy 3	5	-1	1	-
Multi-melta	24"	Heavy 1	8	-4	D6	If the target is within half range of this weapon, roll two dice when inflicting damage with it and discard the lowest result.
Plasma cannon	When attacking with this weapon, choose one of the profiles below.					
- Standard	36"	Heavy D3	7	-3	1	-
- Supercharge	36"	Heavy D3	8	-3	2	On a hit roll of 1, the bearer is slain after all of this weapon's shots have been resolved.
Servo-arm	Melee	Melee	x2	-2	3	Each servo-arm can only be used to make one attack each time this model fights. When a model attacks with this weapon, you must subtract 1 from the hit roll.

WARGEAR OPTIONS

- Up to two models may replace their servo-arm with a heavy bolter, a plasma cannon or a multi-melta.

ABILITIES

Mindlock: Models in this unit improve both their Weapon Skill and Ballistic Skill to 4+, and their Leadership to 9, whilst they are within 6" of any friendly Grey Knights Techmarines.

FACTION KEYWORDS: Imperium, Adeptus Astartes, Grey Knights

KEYWORDS: Infantry, Servitors

8 POWER

Interceptor Squad

NAME	M	WS	BS	S	T	W	A	Ld	Sv
Interceptor	12"	3+	3+	4	4	1	1	7	3+
Interceptor Justicar	12"	3+	3+	4	4	1	2	8	3+

This unit contains 1 Interceptor Justicar and 4 Interceptors. It can include up to 5 additional Interceptors (**Power Rating +8**). Each model is armed with a Nemesis force sword, storm bolter, frag grenades, krak grenades and psyk-out grenades.

WEAPON	RANGE	TYPE	S	AP	D	ABILITIES
Storm bolter	24"	Rapid Fire 2	4	0	1	-
Nemesis force sword	Melee	Melee	User	-3	D3	-
Frag grenade	6"	Grenade D6	3	0	1	-
Krak grenade	6"	Grenade 1	6	-1	D3	-
Psyk-out grenade	6"	Grenade D3	2	0	1	Each time you roll a hit roll of 6+ for this weapon when targeting a PSYKER or DAEMON, the target suffers a mortal wound instead of the normal damage.

WARGEAR OPTIONS

- Any model may replace his Nemesis force sword with an item from the *Melee Weapons* list.
- For every five models in the unit, one Interceptor may replace his Nemesis force sword and storm bolter with an item from the *Special Weapons* list.

ABILITIES

And They Shall Know No Fear, Daemon Hunters, Rites of Banishment, Teleport Strike (pg 62-63)

Combat Squads: Before any models are deployed at the start of the game, an Interceptor Squad containing 10 models may be split into two units, each containing 5 models.

Personal Teleporters: This unit can move across models and terrain as if they were not there. In addition, once per battle, instead of moving this unit normally in the Movement phase, you can choose for them to make a teleport shunt. At the end of the Movement phase, remove all of the models in the unit from the battlefield, then immediately set them up anywhere that is more than 9" from any enemy models.

PSYKER

This unit can attempt to manifest one psychic power in each friendly Psychic phase, and attempt to deny one psychic power in each enemy Psychic phase. It knows the *Smite* psychic power and one psychic power from the Sanctic discipline (pg 101).

When manifesting or denying a psychic power, first select a model in the unit – measure range, visibility, etc. from this model. If this unit suffers Perils of the Warp, it suffers D3 mortal wounds as described in the core rules, but units within 6" will only suffer damage if the Perils of the Warp cause the last model in the manifesting unit to be slain.

FACTION KEYWORDS IMPERIUM, ADEPTUS ASTARTES, GREY KNIGHTS

KEYWORDS INFANTRY, PSYKER, INTERCEPTOR SQUAD

Equipped with personal teleporters, Interceptor Squads can cover great distances and avoid obstacles by shifting through the warp.

Purgation Squads are armed with the Chapter's most devastating heavy weapons, including priceless psycannons and psilencers.

7 POWER

Purgation Squad

NAME	M	WS	BS	S	T	W	A	Ld	Sv
Purgator	6"	3+	3+	4	4	1	1	7	3+
Purgator Justicar	6"	3+	3+	4	4	1	2	8	3+

This unit contains 1 Purgator Justicar and 4 Purgators. It can include up to 5 additional Purgators (**Power Rating +7**). Each model is armed with a Nemesis force sword, storm bolter, frag grenades, krak grenades and psyk-out grenades.

WEAPON	RANGE	TYPE	S	AP	D	ABILITIES
Storm bolter	24"	Rapid Fire 2	4	0	1	-
Nemesis force sword	Melee	Melee	User	-3	D3	-
Frag grenade	6"	Grenade D6	3	0	1	-
Krak grenade	6"	Grenade 1	6	-1	D3	-
Psyk-out grenade	6"	Grenade D3	2	0	1	Each time you roll a hit roll of 6+ for this weapon when targeting a PSYKER or DAEMON, the target suffers a mortal wound instead of the normal damage.

WARGEAR OPTIONS

- Any model may replace his Nemesis force sword with an item from the *Melee Weapons* list.
- Up to four Purgators in the unit may replace their Nemesis force sword and storm bolter with an item from the *Special Weapons* list.

ABILITIES

And They Shall Know No Fear, Daemon Hunters, Rites of Banishment (pg 62)

Combat Squads: Before any models are deployed at the start of the game, a Purgation Squad containing 10 models may be split into two units, each containing 5 models.

PSYKER

This unit can attempt to manifest one psychic power in each friendly Psychic phase, and attempt to deny one psychic power in each enemy Psychic phase. It knows the *Smite* psychic power and one psychic power from the Sanctic discipline (pg 101).

When manifesting or denying a psychic power, first select a model in the unit – measure range, visibility, etc. from this model. If this unit suffers Perils of the Warp, it suffers D3 mortal wounds as described in the core rules, but units within 6" will only suffer damage if the Perils of the Warp cause the last model in the manifesting unit to be slain.

FACTION KEYWORDS IMPERIUM, ADEPTUS ASTARTES, GREY KNIGHTS

KEYWORDS INFANTRY, PSYKER, PURGATION SQUAD

11 POWER

Nemesis Dreadknight

NAME	M	WS	BS	S	T	W	A	Ld	Sv
Nemesis Dreadknight	*	3+	*	6	6	12	*	8	2+

A Nemesis Dreadknight is a single model equipped with two dreadfists.

DAMAGE
Some of this model's characteristics change as it suffers damage, as shown below:

REMAINING W	M	BS	A
7-12+	8"	3+	4
4-6	7"	4+	3
1-3	6"	5+	2

WEAPON	RANGE	TYPE	S	AP	D	ABILITIES
Gatling psilencer	24"	Heavy 12	4	0	D3	-
Heavy incinerator	12"	Heavy D6	6	-1	2	This weapon automatically hits its target.
Heavy psycannon	24"	Heavy 6	7	-1	2	-
Dreadfist	Melee	Melee	x2	-3	D3	If a model is equipped with two dreadfists, each time it fights it can make 1 additional attack with them.
Nemesis Daemon greathammer	Melee	Melee	x2	-4	D6	When a model attacks with this weapon, you must subtract 1 from the hit roll. Damage rolls of less than 3 count as 3 for this weapon.
Nemesis greatsword	Melee	Melee	+4	-3	D6	-

WARGEAR OPTIONS

- This model may take up to two different weapons from the following:
  - Heavy incinerator
  - Gatling psilencer
  - Heavy psycannon
- This model may replace one of its dreadfists with a Nemesis Daemon greathammer or a Nemesis greatsword.
- This model may take a Dreadknight teleporter.

ABILITIES

And They Shall Know No Fear, Daemon Hunters, Rites of Banishment (pg 62)

Force Shielding: This model has a 5+ invulnerable save.

Dreadknight Teleporter: If this model has a Dreadknight teleporter, then during deployment, you can set it up in a teleportarium chamber instead of placing it on the battlefield. At the end of any of your Movement phases this model can teleport into battle – set it up anywhere on the battlefield that is more than 9" away from any enemy models.

PSYKER

This model can attempt to manifest one psychic power in each friendly Psychic phase, and attempt to deny one psychic power in each enemy Psychic phase. It knows the *Smite* psychic power and one psychic power from the Sanctic discipline (pg 101).

FACTION KEYWORDS

Imperium, Adeptus Astartes, Grey Knights

KEYWORDS

Vehicle, Psyker, Nemesis Dreadknight

The Nemesis Dreadknight augments the strength of its Grey Knight pilot, so that he may duel even a mighty Greater Daemon.

19 POWER

Land Raider

DAMAGE
Some of this model's characteristics change as it suffers damage, as shown below:

REMAINING W	M	BS	A
9-16+	10"	3+	6
5-8	5"	4+	D6
1-4	3"	5+	1

NAME	M	WS	BS	S	T	W	A	Ld	Sv
Land Raider	*	6+	*	8	8	16	*	9	2+

A Land Raider is a single model equipped with a twin heavy bolter and two twin lascannons.

WEAPON	RANGE	TYPE	S	AP	D	ABILITIES
Hunter-killer missile	48"	Heavy 1	8	-2	D6	This weapon can only be fired once per battle.
Multi-melta	24"	Heavy 1	8	-4	D6	If the target is within half range of this weapon, roll two dice when inflicting damage with it and discard the lowest result.
Storm bolter	24"	Rapid Fire 2	4	0	1	-
Twin heavy bolter	36"	Heavy 6	5	-1	1	-
Twin lascannon	48"	Heavy 2	9	-3	D6	-

WARGEAR OPTIONS
- This model may take a hunter-killer missile.
- This model may take a storm bolter.
- This model may take a multi-melta.

ABILITIES

Smoke Launchers: Once per game, instead of shooting any weapons in the Shooting phase, this model can use its smoke launchers; until your next Shooting phase your opponent must subtract 1 from all hit rolls for ranged weapons that target this vehicle.

Power of the Machine Spirit: This model does not suffer the penalty to hit rolls for moving and firing Heavy weapons.

Explodes: If this model is reduced to 0 wounds, roll a D6 before removing it from the battlefield and before any embarked models disembark. On a 6 it explodes, and each unit within 6" suffers D6 mortal wounds.

TRANSPORT
This model can transport 10 Grey Knights Infantry models. Each Terminator model takes the space of 2 other infantry models.

FACTION KEYWORDS
Imperium, Adeptus Astartes, Grey Knights

KEYWORDS
Vehicle, Transport, Land Raider

Land Raider Crusader

16 Power

NAME	M	WS	BS	S	T	W	A	Ld	Sv
Land Raider Crusader	*	6+	*	8	8	16	*	9	2+

DAMAGE
Some of this model's characteristics change as it suffers damage, as shown below:

REMAINING W	M	BS	A
9-16+	10"	3+	6
5-8	5"	4+	D6
1-4	3"	5+	1

A Land Raider Crusader is a single model equipped with a twin assault cannon and two hurricane bolters.

WEAPON	RANGE	TYPE	S	AP	D	ABILITIES
Hunter-killer missile	48"	Heavy 1	8	-2	D6	This weapon can only be fired once per battle.
Hurricane bolter	24"	Rapid Fire 6	4	0	1	-
Multi-melta	24"	Heavy 1	8	-4	D6	If the target is within half range of this weapon, roll two dice when inflicting damage with it and discard the lowest result.
Storm bolter	24"	Rapid Fire 2	4	0	1	-
Twin assault cannon	24"	Heavy 12	6	-1	1	-

WARGEAR OPTIONS
- This model may take a hunter-killer missile.
- This model may take a storm bolter.
- This model may take a multi-melta.

ABILITIES

Smoke Launchers: Once per game, instead of shooting any weapons in the Shooting phase, this model can use its smoke launchers; until your next Shooting phase your opponent must subtract 1 from all hit rolls for ranged weapons that target this vehicle.

Frag Assault Launchers: Roll a D6 each time this model finishes a charge move within 1" of an enemy unit; on a 4+ that unit suffers D3 mortal wounds.

Power of the Machine Spirit: This model does not suffer the penalty to hit rolls for moving and firing Heavy weapons.

Explodes: If this model is reduced to 0 wounds, roll a D6 before removing it from the battlefield and before any embarked models disembark. On a 6 it explodes, and each unit within 6" suffers D6 mortal wounds.

TRANSPORT
This model can transport 16 Grey Knights Infantry models. Each Terminator model takes the space of 2 other infantry models.

FACTION KEYWORDS
Imperium, Adeptus Astartes, Grey Knights

KEYWORDS
Vehicle, Transport, Land Raider, Land Raider Crusader

Crusader-pattern Land Raiders are designed to smash their way through enemy fortifications before disgorging troops into the breach.

The Land Raider Redeemer is armed with huge flamestorm cannons, the better to burn the forces of Chaos from their lairs.

18 POWER

Land Raider Redeemer

NAME	M	WS	BS	S	T	W	A	Ld	Sv
Land Raider Redeemer	*	6+	*	8	8	16	*	9	2+

A Land Raider Redeemer is a single model equipped with a twin assault cannon and two flamestorm cannons.

DAMAGE
Some of this model's characteristics change as it suffers damage, as shown below:

REMAINING W	M	BS	A
9-16+	10"	3+	6
5-8	5"	4+	D6
1-4	3"	5+	1

WEAPON	RANGE	TYPE	S	AP	D	ABILITIES
Flamestorm cannon	8"	Heavy D6	6	-2	2	This weapon automatically hits its target.
Hunter-killer missile	48"	Heavy 1	8	-2	D6	This weapon can only be fired once per battle.
Multi-melta	24"	Heavy 1	8	-4	D6	If the target is within half range of this weapon, roll two dice when inflicting damage with it and discard the lowest result.
Storm bolter	24"	Rapid Fire 2	4	0	1	-
Twin assault cannon	24"	Heavy 12	6	-1	1	-

WARGEAR OPTIONS

- This model may take a hunter-killer missile.
- This model may take a storm bolter.
- This model may take a multi-melta.

ABILITIES

Power of the Machine Spirit: This model does not suffer the penalty to hit rolls for moving and firing Heavy weapons.

Frag Assault Launchers: Roll a D6 each time this model finishes a charge move within 1" of an enemy unit; on a 4+ that unit suffers D3 mortal wounds.

Smoke Launchers: Once per game, instead of shooting any weapons in the Shooting phase, this model can use its smoke launchers; until your next Shooting phase your opponent must subtract 1 from all hit rolls for ranged weapons that target this vehicle.

Explodes: If this model is reduced to 0 wounds, roll a D6 before removing it from the battlefield and before any embarked models disembark. On a 6 it explodes, and each unit within 6" suffers D6 mortal wounds.

TRANSPORT

This model can transport 12 Grey Knights Infantry models. Each Terminator model takes the space of 2 other infantry models.

FACTION KEYWORDS

Imperium, Adeptus Astartes, Grey Knights

KEYWORDS

Vehicle, Transport, Land Raider, Land Raider Redeemer

5 POWER

Razorback

NAME	M	WS	BS	S	T	W	A	Ld	Sv
Razorback	*	6+	*	6	7	10	*	8	3+

DAMAGE
Some of this model's characteristics change as it suffers damage, as shown below:

REMAINING W	M	BS	A
6-10+	12"	3+	3
3-5	6"	4+	D3
1-2	3"	5+	1

A Razorback is a single model equipped with a twin heavy bolter.

WEAPON	RANGE	TYPE	S	AP	D	ABILITIES
Hunter-killer missile	48"	Heavy 1	8	-2	D6	This weapon can only be fired once per battle.
Storm bolter	24"	Rapid Fire 2	4	0	1	-
Twin assault cannon	24"	Heavy 12	6	-1	1	-
Twin heavy bolter	36"	Heavy 6	5	-1	1	-
Twin lascannon	48"	Heavy 2	9	-3	D6	-

WARGEAR OPTIONS
- This model may replace its twin heavy bolter with a twin lascannon or a twin assault cannon.
- This model may take a hunter-killer missile.
- This model may take a storm bolter.

ABILITIES

Explodes: If this model is reduced to 0 wounds, roll a D6 before removing it from the battlefield and before any embarked models disembark. On a 6 it explodes, and each unit within 6" suffers D3 mortal wounds.

Smoke Launchers: Once per game, instead of shooting any weapons in the Shooting phase, this model can use its smoke launchers; until your next Shooting phase your opponent must subtract 1 from all hit rolls for ranged weapons that target this vehicle.

TRANSPORT
This model can transport 6 GREY KNIGHTS INFANTRY models, but it cannot transport any TERMINATOR models.

FACTION KEYWORDS
IMPERIUM, ADEPTUS ASTARTES, GREY KNIGHTS

KEYWORDS
VEHICLE, TRANSPORT, RAZORBACK

4 POWER

Rhino

NAME	M	WS	BS	S	T	W	A	Ld	Sv
Rhino	*	6+	*	6	7	10	*	8	3+

DAMAGE
Some of this model's characteristics change as it suffers damage, as shown below:

REMAINING W	M	BS	A
6-10+	12"	3+	3
3-5	6"	4+	D3
1-2	3"	5+	1

A Rhino is a single model equipped with a storm bolter.

WEAPON	RANGE	TYPE	S	AP	D	ABILITIES
Hunter-killer missile	48"	Heavy 1	8	-2	D6	This weapon can only be fired once per battle.
Storm bolter	24"	Rapid Fire 2	4	0	1	-

WARGEAR OPTIONS
- This model may take a hunter-killer missile.

ABILITIES

Smoke Launchers: Once per game, instead of shooting any weapons in the Shooting phase, this model can use its smoke launchers; until your next Shooting phase your opponent must subtract 1 from all hit rolls for ranged weapons that target this vehicle.

Self-Repair: Roll a D6 at the start of each of your turns; on a 6, this model regains one lost wound.

Explodes: If this model is reduced to 0 wounds, roll a D6 before removing it from the battlefield and before any embarked models disembark. On a 6 it explodes, and each unit within 6" suffers D3 mortal wounds.

TRANSPORT
This model can transport 10 GREY KNIGHTS INFANTRY models, but it cannot transport any TERMINATOR models.

FACTION KEYWORDS
IMPERIUM, ADEPTUS ASTARTES, GREY KNIGHTS

KEYWORDS
VEHICLE, TRANSPORT, RHINO

10 POWER

Stormhawk Interceptor

NAME	M	WS	BS	S	T	W	A	Ld	Sv
Stormhawk Interceptor	*	6+	*	6	7	10	*	8	3+

DAMAGE
Some of this model's characteristics change as it suffers damage, as shown below:

REMAINING W	M	BS	A
6-10+	20-60"	3+	3
3-5	20-40"	4+	D3
1-2	20-25"	5+	1

A Stormhawk Interceptor is a single model equipped with two assault cannons, two heavy bolters and an Icarus stormcannon.

WEAPON	RANGE	TYPE	S	AP	D	ABILITIES
Assault cannon	24"	Heavy 6	6	-1	1	-
Heavy bolter	36"	Heavy 3	5	-1	1	-
Icarus stormcannon	48"	Heavy 3	7	-1	2	Add 1 to hit rolls made for this weapon when it targets units that can FLY. Subtract 1 from hit rolls made for this weapon against all other targets.
Las-talon	24"	Heavy 2	9	-3	D6	-
Skyhammer missile launcher	60"	Heavy 3	7	-1	D3	Add 1 to hit rolls made for this weapon when it targets units that can FLY. Subtract 1 from hit rolls made for this weapon against all other targets.
Typhoon missile launcher	When attacking with this weapon, choose one of the profiles below.					
- Frag missile	48"	Heavy 2D6	4	0	1	-
- Krak missile	48"	Heavy 2	8	-2	D6	-

WARGEAR OPTIONS

- This model may replace its two heavy bolters with a skyhammer missile launcher or a typhoon missile launcher.
- This model may replace its Icarus stormcannon with a las-talon.

ABILITIES

Airborne: This model cannot charge, can only be charged by units that can FLY, and can only attack or be attacked in the Fight phase by units that can FLY.

Crash and Burn: If this model is reduced to 0 wounds, roll a D6 before removing the model from the battlefield; on a 6 it crashes and explodes, and each unit within 6" suffers D3 mortal wounds.

Interceptor: You can add 1 to hit rolls for this model when targeting an enemy in the Shooting phase that can FLY.

Supersonic: Each time this model moves, first pivot it on the spot up to 90° (this does not contribute to how far the model moves), and then move the model straight forwards. Note that it cannot pivot again after the initial pivot. When this model Advances, increase its Move characteristic by 20" until the end of the phase – do not roll a dice.

Hard to Hit: Your opponent must subtract 1 from hit rolls for attacks that target this model in the Shooting phase.

Infernum Halo-launcher: You can re-roll save rolls of 1 for this model.

FACTION KEYWORDS IMPERIUM, ADEPTUS ASTARTES, GREY KNIGHTS

KEYWORDS VEHICLE, FLY, STORMHAWK INTERCEPTOR

Manoeuvrable and heavily armed, the Stormhawk Interceptor is the perfect vessel with which to dominate the skies above a battlefield.

15 POWER

Stormraven Gunship

NAME	M	WS	BS	S	T	W	A	Ld	Sv
Stormraven Gunship	*	6+	*	8	7	14	*	9	3+

DAMAGE
Some of this model's characteristics change as it suffers damage, as shown below:

REMAINING W	M	BS	A
8-14+	20-45"	3+	3
4-7	20-30"	4+	D3
1-3	20"	5+	1

A Stormraven Gunship is a single model equipped with a twin assault cannon, a twin heavy bolter and two stormstrike missile launchers.

WEAPON	RANGE	TYPE	S	AP	D	ABILITIES
Hurricane bolter	24"	Rapid Fire 6	4	0	1	-
Stormstrike missile launcher	72"	Heavy 1	8	-3	3	-
Twin assault cannon	24"	Heavy 12	6	-1	1	-
Twin heavy bolter	36"	Heavy 6	5	-1	1	-
Twin heavy plasma cannon	When attacking with this weapon, choose one of the profiles below.					
- Standard	36"	Heavy 2D3	7	-3	1	-
- Supercharge	36"	Heavy 2D3	8	-3	2	For each hit roll of 1, the bearer suffers 1 mortal wound after all of this weapon's shots have been resolved.
Twin lascannon	48"	Heavy 2	9	-3	D6	-
Twin multi-melta	24"	Heavy 2	8	-4	D6	If the target is within half range of this weapon, roll two dice when inflicting damage with it and discard the lowest result.
Typhoon missile launcher	When attacking with this weapon, choose one of the profiles below.					
- Frag missile	48"	Heavy 2D6	4	0	1	-
- Krak missile	48"	Heavy 2	8	-2	D6	-

WARGEAR OPTIONS

- This model may replace its twin assault cannon with a twin lascannon or a twin heavy plasma cannon.
- This model may replace its twin heavy bolter with a twin multi-melta or a typhoon missile launcher.
- This model may take two hurricane bolters.

ABILITIES

Airborne: This model cannot charge, can only be charged by units that can Fly, and can only attack or be attacked in the Fight phase by units that can Fly.

Supersonic: Each time this model moves, first pivot it on the spot up to 90° (this does not contribute to how far the model moves), and then move the model straight forwards. Note that it cannot pivot again after the initial pivot. When this model Advances, increase its Move characteristic by 20" until the end of the phase – do not roll a dice.

Hard to Hit: Your opponent must subtract 1 from hit rolls for attacks that target this model in the Shooting phase.

Hover Jet: Before this model moves in your Movement phase, you can declare it will hover. Its Move characteristic becomes 20" until the end of the phase, and it loses the Airborne, Hard to Hit and Supersonic abilities until the beginning of your next Movement phase.

Crash and Burn: If this model is reduced to 0 wounds, roll a D6 before removing the model from the battlefield and before any embarked models disembark. On a 6 it crashes and explodes, and each unit within 6" suffers D3 mortal wounds.

Power of the Machine Spirit: This model does not suffer the penalty to hit rolls for moving and firing Heavy weapons.

TRANSPORT

This model can transport 12 Grey Knights Infantry models and 1 Grey Knights Dreadnought. Each Terminator model takes the space of two other infantry models.

FACTION KEYWORDS

Imperium, Adeptus Astartes, Grey Knights

KEYWORDS

Vehicle, Transport, Fly, Stormraven Gunship

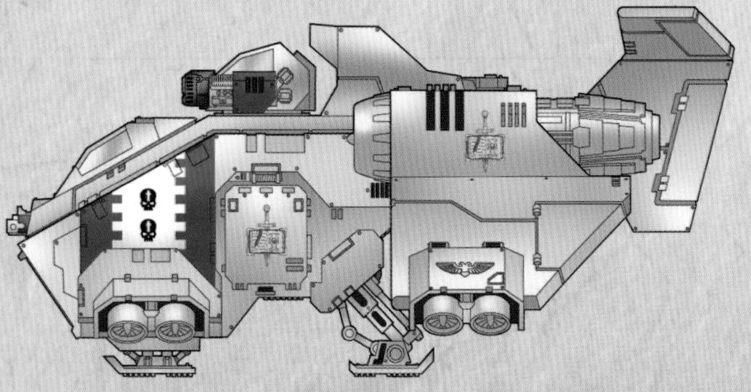

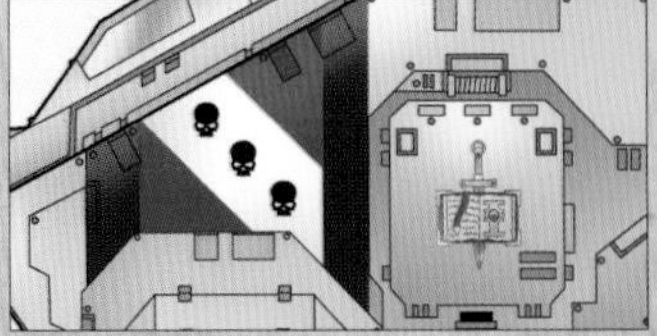

Like Land Raiders, Grey Knights aerial support vehicles bear the heraldry of their Techmarine pilots. Squadrons are distinguished by a unifying colour on wings or weapon cowlings.

9 POWER

Stormtalon Gunship

NAME	M	WS	BS	S	T	W	A	Ld	Sv
Stormtalon Gunship	*	6+	*	6	6	10	*	8	3+

A Stormtalon Gunship is a single model equipped with a twin assault cannon and two heavy bolters.

DAMAGE
Some of this model's characteristics change as it suffers damage, as shown below:

REMAINING W	M	BS	A
6-10+	20-50"	3+	3
3-5	20-35"	4+	D3
1-2	20"	5+	1

WEAPON	RANGE	TYPE	S	AP	D	ABILITIES
Heavy bolter	36"	Heavy 3	5	-1	1	-
Lascannon	48"	Heavy 1	9	-3	D6	-
Skyhammer missile launcher	60"	Heavy 3	7	-1	D3	Add 1 to hit rolls made for this weapon when it targets units that can FLY. Subtract 1 from hit rolls made for this weapon against all other targets.
Twin assault cannon	24"	Heavy 12	6	-1	1	-
Typhoon missile launcher	When attacking with this weapon, choose one of the profiles below.					
- Frag missile	48"	Heavy 2D6	4	0	1	-
- Krak missile	48"	Heavy 2	8	-2	D6	-

WARGEAR OPTIONS

- This model may replace its two heavy bolters with two lascannons, a skyhammer missile launcher or a typhoon missile launcher.

ABILITIES

Airborne: This model cannot charge, can only be charged by units that can FLY, and can only attack or be attacked in the Fight phase by units that can FLY.

Supersonic: Each time this model moves, first pivot it on the spot up to 90° (this does not contribute to how far the model moves), and then move the model straight forwards. Note that it cannot pivot again after the initial pivot. When this model Advances, increase its Move characteristic by 20" until the end of the phase – do not roll a dice.

Hard to Hit: Your opponent must subtract 1 from hit rolls for attacks that target this model in the Shooting phase.

Strafing Run: You can add 1 to hit rolls for this model when targeting an enemy in the Shooting phase that cannot FLY.

Hover Jet: Before this model moves in your Movement phase, you can declare it will hover. Its Move characteristic becomes 20" until the end of the phase, and it loses the Airborne, Hard to Hit and Supersonic abilities until the beginning of your next Movement phase.

Crash and Burn: If this model is reduced to 0 wounds, roll a D6 before removing the model from the battlefield; on a 6 it crashes and explodes, and each unit within 6" suffers D3 mortal wounds.

FACTION KEYWORDS IMPERIUM, ADEPTUS ASTARTES, GREY KNIGHTS

KEYWORDS VEHICLE, FLY, STORMTALON GUNSHIP

Stormtalon Gunships are versatile and deadly, as well suited to strafing ground targets as they are to flying escort missions.

ARMOURY OF TITAN

As Space Marines, the Grey Knights utilise a number of weapons common to every Chapter, but their role as the Imperium's foremost Daemon-hunters requires them to make use of powerful, often psychically enhanced wargear forged especially for this purpose. The profiles for all of their weapons are detailed below.

RANGED WEAPONS						
WEAPON	**RANGE**	**TYPE**	**S**	**AP**	**D**	**ABILITIES**
Assault cannon	24"	Heavy 6	6	-1	1	-
Bolt pistol	12"	Pistol 1	4	0	1	-
Boltgun	24"	Rapid Fire 1	4	0	1	-
Combi-flamer	When attacking with this weapon, choose one or both of the profiles below. If you choose both, subtract 1 from all hit rolls made for this weapon.					
- Boltgun	24"	Rapid Fire 1	4	0	1	-
- Flamer	8"	Assault D6	4	0	1	This weapon automatically hits its target.
Combi-melta	When attacking with this weapon, choose one or both of the profiles below. If you choose both, subtract 1 from all hit rolls made for this weapon.					
- Boltgun	24"	Rapid Fire 1	4	0	1	-
- Meltagun	12"	Assault 1	8	-4	D6	If the target is within half range of this weapon, roll two dice when inflicting damage with it and discard the lowest result.
Combi-plasma	When attacking with this weapon, choose one or both of the profiles below. If you choose both, subtract 1 from all hit rolls made for this weapon.					
- Boltgun	24"	Rapid Fire 1	4	0	1	-
- Plasma gun	24"	Rapid Fire 1	7	-3	1	This weapon can be supercharged by the bearer before firing. If they do so, increase the Strength and Damage of the weapon by 1 this turn. On any hit rolls of 1 when firing supercharge, the bearer is slain after all of the weapon's shots have been resolved.
Flamer	8"	Assault D6	4	0	1	This weapon automatically hits its target.
Flamestorm cannon	8"	Heavy D6	6	-2	2	This weapon automatically hits its target.
Frag grenade	6"	Grenade D6	3	0	1	-
Gatling psilencer	24"	Heavy 12	4	0	D3	-
Heavy bolter	36"	Heavy 3	5	-1	1	-
Heavy flamer	8"	Heavy D6	5	-1	1	This weapon automatically hits its target.
Heavy incinerator	12"	Heavy D6	6	-1	2	This weapon automatically hits its target.
Heavy plasma cannon	When attacking with this weapon, choose one of the profiles below.					
- Standard	36"	Heavy D3	7	-3	1	-
- Supercharge	36"	Heavy D3	8	-3	2	For each hit roll of 1, the bearer suffers 1 mortal wound after all of this weapon's shots have been resolved.
Heavy psycannon	24"	Heavy 6	7	-1	2	-
Hunter-killer missile	48"	Heavy 1	8	-2	D6	This weapon can only be fired once per battle.
Hurricane bolter	24"	Rapid Fire 6	4	0	1	-
Icarus stormcannon	48"	Heavy 3	7	-1	2	Add 1 to hit rolls made for this weapon when it targets units that can FLY. Subtract 1 from hit rolls made for this weapon against all other targets.
Incinerator	8"	Assault D6	6	-1	1	This weapon automatically hits its target.
Krak grenade	6"	Grenade 1	6	-1	D3	-
Las-talon	24"	Heavy 2	9	-3	D6	-
Lascannon	48"	Heavy 1	9	-3	D6	-
Missile launcher	When attacking with this weapon, choose one of the profiles below.					
- Frag missile	48"	Heavy D6	4	0	1	-
- Krak missile	48"	Heavy 1	8	-2	D6	-
Multi-melta	24"	Heavy 1	8	-4	D6	If the target is within half range of this weapon, roll two dice when inflicting damage with it and discard the lowest result.
Plasma cannon	When attacking with this weapon, choose one of the profiles below.					
- Standard	36"	Heavy D3	7	-3	1	-
- Supercharge	36"	Heavy D3	8	-3	2	On a hit roll of 1, the bearer is slain after all of this weapon's shots have been resolved.

RANGED WEAPONS						
WEAPON	**RANGE**	**TYPE**	**S**	**AP**	**D**	**ABILITIES**
Plasma cutter	When attacking with this weapon, choose one of the profiles below.					
- Standard	12"	Assault 1	7	-3	1	-
- Supercharge	12"	Assault 1	8	-3	2	On a hit roll of 1, the bearer is slain after all of this weapon's shots have been resolved.
Psilencer	24"	Heavy 6	4	0	D3	-
Psycannon	24"	Heavy 4	7	-1	1	-
Psyk-out grenade	6"	Grenade D3	2	0	1	Each time you roll a hit roll of 6+ for this weapon when targeting a PSYKER or DAEMON, the target suffers a mortal wound instead of the normal damage.
Skyhammer missile launcher	60"	Heavy 3	7	-1	D3	Add 1 to hit rolls made for this weapon when it targets units that can FLY. Subtract 1 from hit rolls made for this weapon against all other targets.
Storm bolter	24"	Rapid Fire 2	4	0	1	-
Stormstrike missile launcher	72"	Heavy 1	8	-3	3	-
Twin assault cannon	24"	Heavy 12	6	-1	1	-
Twin heavy bolter	36"	Heavy 6	5	-1	1	-
Twin heavy plasma cannon	When attacking with this weapon, choose one of the profiles below.					
- Standard	36"	Heavy 2D3	7	-3	1	-
- Supercharge	36"	Heavy 2D3	8	-3	2	For each hit roll of 1, the bearer suffers 1 mortal wound after all of this weapon's shots have been resolved.
Twin lascannon	48"	Heavy 2	9	-3	D6	-
Twin multi-melta	24"	Heavy 2	8	-4	D6	If the target is within half range of this weapon, roll two dice when inflicting damage with it and discard the lowest result.
Typhoon missile launcher	When attacking with this weapon, choose one of the profiles below.					
- Frag missile	48"	Heavy 2D6	4	0	1	-
- Krak missile	48"	Heavy 2	8	-2	D6	-

MELEE WEAPONS					
WEAPON	**TYPE**	**S**	**AP**	**D**	**ABILITIES**
The Black Blade of Antwyr	Melee	User	0	1	-
Crozius arcanum	Melee	+1	-1	2	-
Dreadfist	Melee	x2	-3	D3	If a model is equipped with two dreadfists, each time it fights it can make 1 additional attack with them.
Dreadnought combat weapon	Melee	x2	-3	3	-
Malleus Argyrum	Melee	x2	-3	3	-
Nemesis Daemon greathammer	Melee	x2	-4	D6	When a model attacks with this weapon, you must subtract 1 from the hit roll. Damage rolls of less than 3 count as 3 for this weapon.
Nemesis Daemon hammer	Melee	x2	-3	3	When a model attacks with this weapon, you must subtract 1 from the hit roll.
Nemesis falchion	Melee	User	-2	D3	If a model is armed with two Nemesis falchions, each time it fights it can make 1 additional attack with them.
Nemesis force halberd	Melee	+1	-2	D3	-
Nemesis force sword	Melee	User	-3	D3	-
Nemesis greatsword	Melee	+4	-3	D6	-
Nemesis warding stave	Melee	+2	-1	D3	A model armed with this weapon has a 5+ invulnerable save against attacks made in the Fight phase. If it already has an invulnerable save, add 1 to invulnerable saving throws you make for it in the Fight phase instead.
Power axe	Melee	+1	-2	1	-
Servo-arm	Melee	x2	-2	3	Each servo-arm can only be used to make one attack each time this model fights. When a model attacks with this weapon, you must subtract 1 from the hit roll.
The Titansword	Melee	+4	-4	3	-

AEGIS
TERRA
TITAN
AEGIS
TERRA
TITAN
MORTIS

As their Gunships and Interceptors scream overhead, the stalwart warriors of the Grey Knights stride into battle against a seething tide of Khornate Daemons. Silver armour gleams, and proud heraldry stands out against the hellish light of battle, each Grey Knight a beacon of purity amidst an ocean of corruption.

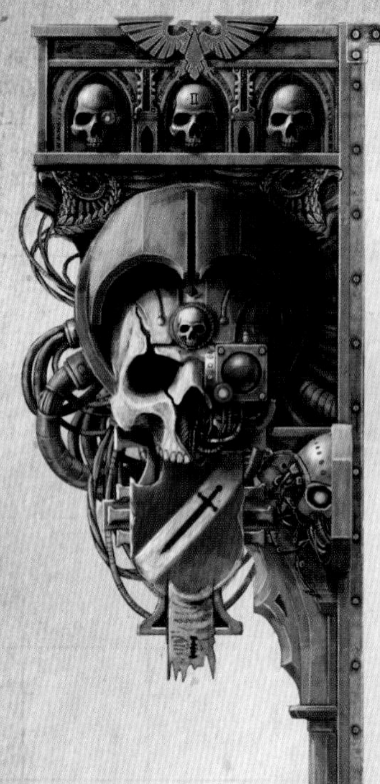

THE HAMMER OF DAEMONS

In this section you'll find rules for Battle-forged armies that include Grey Knights Detachments – that is, any Detachment which includes only Grey Knights units. These rules include the abilities below and a series of Stratagems that can only be used by the Grey Knights. This section also includes the Grey Knights' unique Warlord Traits, Psychic Discipline, Relics and Tactical Objectives. Together, these rules reflect the character and fighting style of the Grey Knights in your games of Warhammer 40,000.

BROTHERHOOD OF PSYKERS

Clad in warded armour and engaged in gestalt psychic communion, an army of Grey Knights is girded well against the powers of the warp.

If your army is Battle-forged, all **Psykers** in **Grey Knights** Detachments gain this ability. You can add 1 to Psychic tests and Deny the Witch tests taken for such a unit.

KNIGHTS OF TITAN

Strike Squads and Terminator Squads form the backbone of many Grey Knights armies, and it is their duty to control vital objectives.

If your army is Battle-forged, all Troops units in **Grey Knights** Detachments gain this ability. Such a unit that is within range of an objective marker (as specified in the mission) controls that objective marker even if there are more enemy models within range of that objective marker. If an enemy unit within range of the same objective marker has a similar ability, then the objective marker is controlled by the player who has the most models within range of it as normal.

'The weak will always be led by the strong. Where the strong see purpose and act, the weak follow; where the strong cry out against fate, the weak bow their heads and succumb. There are many who are weak; and many are their temptations. Despise the weak for they shall flock to the call of the Daemon and the Renegade. Pity them not and scorn their cries of innocence – it is better that one hundred innocently fall before the wrath of the Emperor than one kneels before the Daemon.'

- Excerpt from The First Book of Indoctrinations

WARLORD TRAITS

The commanders of the Grey Knights are mighty warriors and gifted tacticians all, and their specialised style of warfare calls for them to become seasoned in unique skills, be they mental or physical.

If a GREY KNIGHTS CHARACTER is your Warlord, he can generate a Warlord Trait from the following table instead of the one in the *Warhammer 40,000* rulebook. You can either roll on the table below to randomly generate a Warlord Trait, or you can select the one that best suits his temperament and preferred style of waging war.

D6 RESULT

1 DAEMON-SLAYER

The Warlord is a master of the rituals of banishing and unbinding, able to sever his daemonic foes' connection to the warp.

If your Warlord wounds a DAEMON in the Fight phase, your opponent must subtract 1 from any invulnerable saving throws made against the attack.

2 HAMMER OF RIGHTEOUSNESS

Fortified by the unflagging will of his battle-brothers, the Warlord charges into the foe like the hammer of the Emperor.

You can add 1 to wound rolls for your Warlord in the Fight phase if he successfully charged this turn.

3 UNYIELDING ANVIL

The inspiring presence of the Warlord reminds the Grey Knights that there can be no retreat, no matter the odds arrayed against them.

Friendly GREY KNIGHTS units that are within 6" of your Warlord automatically pass Morale tests.

4 FIRST TO THE FRAY

The Warlord is an eager, hot-blooded warrior, ever the first to leap into the fray. Inspired by such zealous bravery, his battle-brothers are never far behind.

You can re-roll failed charge rolls for your Warlord and friendly GREY KNIGHTS units that are within 6" of him at the start of the Charge phase.

5 NEMESIS LORD

Over the course of countless battles the Warlord has mastered the art of single combat. He is a force of destruction upon the battlefield, wielding his Nemesis weapon with preternatural skill.

You can add 1 to the Damage characteristic of your Warlord's melee weapons. If your Warlord wields a Relic of Titan that is a melee weapon, choose another Warlord Trait or re-roll this result.

6 LORE MASTER

The Warlord is a psyker of prodigious strength, a master of his craft who has spent a lifetime learning the forbidden lore of the warp.

Your Warlord knows one additional psychic power from the Sanctic discipline (pg 101).

NAMED CHARACTERS AND WARLORD TRAITS

Many of the Chapter's greatest heroes are renowned as much for their methodology as they are for their deeds on the battlefield. If one of the following named characters is your Warlord, they must be given the associated Warlord Trait shown below.

NAMED CHARACTER	WARLORD TRAIT
Lord Kaldor Draigo	Daemon-slayer
Grand Master Voldus	Lore Master
Castellan Crowe	Hammer of Righteousness
Brother-Captain Stern	Unyielding Anvil

'THE COURAGE SHOWN BY THE MEN AND WOMEN OF THE COMPANY WAS INSPIRATIONAL. THEY CARRIED OUT THEIR DUTY TO THE EMPEROR WITH EXEMPLARY DETERMINATION AND SKILL. IN DIFFICULT CIRCUMSTANCES THEY MANAGED TO ACQUIT THEMSELVES IN THE MANNER EXPECTED OF THE REGIMENT. THE SELFLESSNESS AND SACRIFICE DEMONSTRATED BY THE ENTIRE COMPANY IS, AND WILL REMAIN, A SHINING EXAMPLE OF BRAVERY. THERE WERE NO SURVIVORS OF THE ACTION.'

- Approved Records Text: for posthumous use by units attached to the Grey Knights

STRATAGEMS

If your army is Battle-forged and includes any Grey Knights Detachments (excluding Auxiliary Support Detachments), you have access to the Stratagems shown below, meaning you can spend Command Points to activate them. These help to reflect the unique tactics and strategies used by the Grey Knights on the battlefield.

1CP

TACTICAL FLEXIBILITY

Grey Knights Stratagem

The gestalt psychic consciousness of Grey Knights allows them to react to changing battlefield circumstances almost instantly.

Use this Stratagem at the start of any of your Movement phases. Select a friendly **Grey Knights** unit with the Combat Squads ability that has 10 models. That unit is immediately split into two separate units, each containing 5 models.

1CP

TRUESILVER ARMOUR

Grey Knights Stratagem

Grey Knights vehicles incorporate hexagrammatic runes, litanies of purity, strands of sanctified silver and other sacred wards.

Use this Stratagem when a **Grey Knights Vehicle** suffers a mortal wound. Roll a D6 for that mortal wound, and each other mortal wound inflicted on this model for the rest of the phase. On a 5+ that mortal wound is ignored.

1CP

ONLY IN DEATH DOES DUTY END

Grey Knights Stratagem

A Grey Knight knows that his service to Humanity will likely end in his bloody death. He knows too the importance of ensuring that his final moments cost the enemy dear.

Use this Stratagem when a **Grey Knights Character** is slain. Before removing it from the battlefield, that model can immediately either shoot as if it were his Shooting phase, or fight as if it were his Fight phase.

3CP

HONOUR THE CHAPTER

Grey Knights Stratagem

While the Sons of Titan fight, the Emperor's legacy lives on.

Use this Stratagem at the end of any Fight phase. Select a **Grey Knights Infantry** unit – that unit can immediately fight for a second time.

1CP

WISDOM OF THE ANCIENTS

Grey Knights Stratagem

Grey Knights Dreadnoughts are a link to the Chapter's glorious past. They are living legends, whose mere presence inspires their battle-brothers to great deeds.

Use this Stratagem at the start of any phase. Select a friendly **Grey Knights Dreadnought**. Until the end of the phase you can re-roll hit rolls of 1 for friendly **Grey Knights** units within 6" of that Dreadnought.

1CP

TELEPORTARIUM

Grey Knights Stratagem

The Grey Knights watch from orbit for the perfect moment to strike. Their teleportarium chambers pierce the roiling warp to deliver battle-brothers deep into the heart of the enemy army.

Use this Stratagem during deployment. You can set up a friendly **Grey Knights Infantry** unit or **Grey Knights Dreadnought** in a teleportarium chamber instead of placing it on the battlefield. At the end of any of your Movement phases this unit can teleport into battle – set it up anywhere on the battlefield that is more than 9" away from any enemy models.

1CP

MENTAL FOCUS

Grey Knights Stratagem

Such is the mental discipline of the Grey Knights that even the lowest of their rank can wield the energies of the warp as a weapon. In the midst of a clangorous firefight a battle-brother can shut out all external stimulus, ignoring pain and fear to focus his mind into a reaping blade for the Emperor. By attuning his mind with those of his fellow battle-brothers, a single Grey Knight can bolster his reserve of mental energy and bring his psychic might to bear repeatedly against the enemy or in aid of his allies.

Use this Stratagem in your Psychic phase. One **Grey Knights Psyker** can attempt to cast one additional psychic power this phase.

TELEPORTATION BOOST

1CP

Grey Knights Stratagem

Like a cleansing fire, a squad of Interceptors can sweep across an entire battlefield.

Use this Stratagem in your Movement phase. You can make a teleport shunt with an Interceptor Squad that has already made a teleport shunt earlier in the battle.

PSYCHIC CHANNELLING

1CP

Grey Knights Stratagem

In combat, a Grey Knight can unfetter their psyker's mind.

Use this Stratagem when taking a Psychic test for a **Grey Knights Psyker**. Roll three dice rather than two and pick the two highest rolls.

THE AEGIS

2CP

Grey Knights Stratagem

Upon induction into the Chapter, every Grey Knight is trained to steel himself against psychic assaults.

Use this Stratagem after an enemy **Psyker** has manifested a psychic power within 24" of a **Grey Knights Psyker** or **Grey Knights Vehicle** from your army. Your unit can immediately attempt to Deny the Witch, and when taking the test, roll three dice rather than two and pick the two highest rolls.

HEED THE PROGNOSTICARS

2CP

Grey Knights Stratagem

Wise is the battle-brother who consults the Prognosticars and notes the hour when his mettle will be tested.

Use this Stratagem at the start of your turn. Pick a **Grey Knights Character** and add 1 to its invulnerable saving throws until the start of your next turn.

ARMOURY OF TITAN

1CP/ 3CP

Grey Knights Stratagem

The Chapter's most sacred weapons lie in this hallowed vault.

Use this Stratagem before the battle. Your army can have one extra Relic of Titan for 1 CP, or two extra Relics of Titan for 3 CPs. All of the Relics of Titan that you include must be different and be given to different **Grey Knights Characters**.

ORBITAL BOMBARDMENT

3CP

Grey Knights Stratagem

When needs must, the Grey Knights can call down the awesome firepower of their orbital strike cruisers. A blinding column of energy lances down from the heavens, burning flesh to ash and reducing metal to heaps of molten slag.

This Stratagem can be used once per battle, in the Shooting phase, if you have a **Grey Knights** Warlord that did not move during your Movement phase. Instead of shooting with your Warlord's weapons, select a visible point on the battlefield and roll a D6 for every unit within D6" of that point. Subtract 1 from the result if the unit being rolled for is a **Character**. On a 4+, the unit being rolled for suffers D3 mortal wounds.

PSYCHIC ONSLAUGHT

2CP

Grey Knights Stratagem

Psi weaponry can be used to channel a battle-brother's fury.

Use this Stratagem before a **Grey Knights** unit shoots. The Strength and Armour Penetration characteristics of any gatling psilencers, heavy psycannons, psilencers and psycannons that unit fires are improved by 1 this phase. For example, a psilencer (S4, AP0) would become S5, AP-1.

PSYBOLT AMMUNITION

2CP

Grey Knights Stratagem

By entreating the machine spirit of his weapon with psychic incantations, a battle-brother can infuse the already deadly payload with explosive mental energy.

Use this Stratagem before a **Grey Knights** unit shoots. The Strength and Armour Penetration characteristics of any boltguns, storm bolters, heavy bolters and hurricane bolters that unit fires are improved by 1 this phase. For example, a heavy bolter (S5, AP-1) would become S6, AP-2.

FINEST HOUR

2CP

Grey Knights Stratagem

It is in the darkest times that the disciplined fury of the Grey Knights burns its brightest.

Use this Stratagem at the start of your turn. Pick a **Grey Knights Character** and double the range of any aura abilities on its datasheet (such as Rites of Battle or Bane of Evil) to 12" for this turn.

RELICS OF TITAN

Relics of Titan are items of incredible rarity, be they master-work weapons forged by the tech-artisans of Deimos, or unique artefacts laced with otherworldly power. Some of these relics were first borne into battle by legendary heroes of the Chapter's past, their names synonymous with the mighty deeds of their bearers.

If your army is led by a GREY KNIGHTS Warlord, then before the battle you may give one of the following Relics of Titan to a GREY KNIGHTS CHARACTER. Named characters such as Lord Kaldor Draigo already have one or more artefacts and cannot be given any of the following relics.

Note that some weapons replace one of the character's existing weapons. Where this is the case, if you are playing a matched play game or are otherwise using points values, you must still pay the cost of the weapon that is being replaced. Write down any Relics of Titan your characters have on your army roster.

FURY OF DEIMOS

When the moon of Deimos was gifted to Titan by the Adeptus Mechanicus, it carried with it a ship loaded with some of the finest weapons the Imperium has ever created. Among them was the storm bolter Fury of Deimos, a weapon crafted by the first Fabricator General. Superior in range, accuracy, rate of fire and reliability to a normal storm bolter, it is a relic whose secrets have long been forgotten.

Model with storm bolter only. The Fury of Deimos replaces the bearer's storm bolter and has the following profile:

WEAPON	RANGE	TYPE	S	AP	D
Fury of Deimos	30"	Rapid Fire 3	5	-1	1

DESTROYER OF CRYS'YLLIX

This is the first Nemesis Daemon hammer, upon which all others are based. It was forged by the legendary Reed Vanar, 3rd Brother-Captain of the Exactors, and first used to shatter the Lord of Change known as Crys'yllix. Countless Daemons have felt its wrath in the centuries since.

Model with Nemesis Daemon hammer only. The Destroyer of Crys'yllix replaces the bearer's Nemesis Daemon hammer and has the following profile:

WEAPON	RANGE	TYPE	S	AP	D
Destroyer of Crys'yllix	Melee	Melee	x2	-3	4
Abilities: When a model attacks with this weapon, you must subtract 1 from the hit roll.					

BANNER OF REFINING FLAME

This sacred banner records the most righteous purifications performed by strike forces and individual battle-brothers throughout the Grey Knights' history. The bearer can channel the resonance of this glorious past into his psychic attacks, blasting his foes to ash in a burst of searing light.

Paladin Ancient or Brotherhood Ancient only. The Banner of Refining Flame is a sacred banner. A model equipped with this banner loses the Rites of Banishment ability. Instead, when the bearer manifests the *Smite* psychic power, it only has a range of 6", but it inflicts D6 mortal wounds instead of D3 (whether or not the result of the Psychic test is more than 10).

SOUL GLAIVE

Over centuries of war, a fraction of a Grey Knight's essence may imprint itself upon his weapon. In rare cases, this imprint is so strong that it persists after death, and another can wield the blade to combine their own psychic might with that of a fallen hero. The Soul Glaive is such a weapon, a halberd that was carried into battle by the 13th Supreme Grand Master of the Grey Knights, Lord Sylas Kalthorn, who defeated the Daemon Prince Ka'laedzar in single combat.

Model with Nemesis force halberd only. The Soul Glaive replaces the bearer's Nemesis force halberd and has the following profile:

WEAPON	RANGE	TYPE	S	AP	D
Soul Glaive	Melee	Melee	+1	-3	D3
Abilities: You can re-roll failed hit and wound rolls made for this weapon.					

DOMINA LIBER DAEMONICA

This tome is a relic of Supreme Grand Master Janus, the only Grey Knight to ever master all six hundred and sixty-six words of banishment, each one painstakingly recorded on its pages. In times of need a hero of the Chapter will carry this book into battle, its bindings crackling with arcane energy as the words send Daemons howling back into the warp.

All enemy DAEMON units must subtract 1 from their Leadership characteristic whilst they are within 6" of the bearer.

CUIRASS OF SACRIFICE

The interior of this master-forged suit of armour is etched with the names of the many allies that have fought alongside the Grey Knights. None but the Grey Knights can be trusted to fight the creatures of the warp and remain uncorrupted, so those that battle alongside them rarely survive. The Cuirass is a reminder to the Grey Knights that such sacrifice must not be forgotten, and the wearer swears a solemn vow not to dishonour the names of those who have suffered such a fate whilst even an ounce of strength remains in his body.

INFANTRY model only. Roll a D6 each time the bearer loses a wound. On a 5+, the damage is ignored and the bearer does not lose a wound.

SANCTIC DISCIPLINE

Each Grey Knight is an accomplished psyker, trained to channel his mental energies into protective wards and an array of battle-sorceries. The mightiest Grey Knights of all can banish Daemons with but a touch, conjure psychic defences to protect their allies and unleash the destructive power of the warp itself upon their foes.

Before the battle, generate the psychic powers for PSYKERS that can use powers from the Sanctic discipline using the table below. You can either roll a D6 to generate their powers randomly (re-roll any duplicate results), or you can select the psychic powers you wish the psyker to have.

D6 RESULT

1 PURGE SOUL

The psyker draws upon every ounce of willpower he possesses to purge the evil of his foes' souls, scouring every trace of corruption even if it destroys them in the process.

Purge Soul has a warp charge value of 5. If manifested, pick a visible enemy unit within 12" of the psyker. Both controlling players roll a dice and add their respective unit's highest Leadership value. If the target's total is equal to or greater than the psyker's total, nothing happens. If the psyker's total is greater than the target's total, the target unit suffers a number of mortal wounds equal to the difference.

2 GATE OF INFINITY

The psyker punches a corridor through the roiling immaterium, allowing him to cross great distances in the blink of an eye.

Gate of Infinity has a warp charge value of 6. If manifested, pick a friendly GREY KNIGHTS unit within 12" of the psyker. Remove that unit from the battlefield and immediately set it up anywhere on the battlefield that is more than 9" from any enemy models.

3 HAMMERHAND

Focusing the raging power of his mind, the psyker augments the strength of his comrades to the point where they can crush flesh and bone with a single blow.

Hammerhand has a warp charge value of 6. If manifested, pick a friendly GREY KNIGHTS unit within 12" of the psyker. Add 1 to any wound rolls you make for that unit's Melee weapons until the start of your next Psychic phase.

4 SANCTUARY

Chanting words of warding, the psyker creates a zone of light around him that can both protect him from harm and repel daemonic creatures.

Sanctuary has a warp charge value of 6. If manifested, pick a friendly GREY KNIGHTS unit within 12" of the psyker. That unit gains a 5+ invulnerable save until the start of your next Psychic phase. If any models in the target unit already have an invulnerable save, add 1 to any invulnerable saving throws you make for them until the start of your next Psychic phase instead.

5 ASTRAL AIM

The psyker reaches out to the minds of his fellow battle-brothers, mystically guiding their aim to the chosen target.

Astral Aim has a warp charge value of 5. If manifested, pick a friendly GREY KNIGHTS unit within 18" of the psyker. Until your next Psychic phase, the unit you picked is able to target enemy units that are not visible to them, and units they target with shooting attacks do not gain any bonus to their saving throws for being in cover.

6 VORTEX OF DOOM

The psyker tears a rift between realspace and the warp, condemning his foes to total oblivion.

Vortex of Doom has a warp charge value of 8. If manifested, a vortex opens above the nearest visible enemy model within 12" of the psyker. That model's unit, and every other unit within 3" of that model suffers D3 mortal wounds. The number of mortal wounds inflicted is increased to D6 if the power is manifested with a Psychic test of 12+.

'There are those who might see contradiction between our abhorrence of the Daemon and our wielding of sorcery. Yet those contradictions live only in the minds of weak men, and we are not accountable to such as they.'

- Grand Master Valdar Aurikon

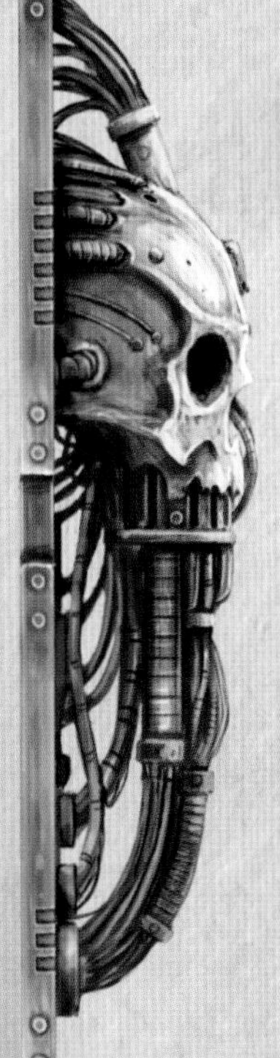

POINTS VALUES

If you are playing a matched play game, or a game that uses a points limit, you can use the following lists to determine the total points cost of your army. Simply add together the points costs of all your models and the wargear they are equipped with to determine your army's total points value.

UNITS

UNIT	MODELS PER UNIT	POINTS PER MODEL (Does not include weapons)
Apothecary	1	90
Brother-Captain	1	150
Brotherhood Ancient	1	128
Brotherhood Champion	1	113
Chaplain	1	144
Dreadnought	1	87
Grand Master	1	160
Grand Master in Nemesis Dreadknight	1	190
Interceptor Squad	5-10	23
Land Raider	1	239
Land Raider Crusader	1	244
Land Raider Redeemer	1	244
Librarian	1	157
Nemesis Dreadknight	1	130
Paladin Ancient	1	140
Paladin Squad	3-10	53
Purgation Squad	5-10	19
Purifier Squad	5-10	26
Razorback	1	65
Rhino	1	70
Servitors	4	2
Stormhawk Interceptor	1	85
Stormraven Gunship	1	172
Stormtalon Gunship	1	110
Strike Squad	5-10	19
Techmarine	1	91
Terminator Squad	5-10	46
Venerable Dreadnought	1	110

UNIQUE UNITS

UNIT	MODELS PER UNIT	POINTS PER MODEL (Includes weapons)
Brother-Captain Stern	1	157
Castellan Crowe	1	125
Grand Master Voldus	1	190
Lord Kaldor Draigo	1	240

RANGED WEAPONS

WEAPON	POINTS PER WEAPON
Assault cannon	21
Bolt pistol	0
Boltgun	0
Combi-flamer	11
Combi-melta	19
Combi-plasma	15
Flamer	9
Flamestorm cannon	30
Frag grenades	0
Gatling psilencer	20
Heavy bolter	10
Heavy flamer	17
Heavy incinerator	40
Heavy plasma cannon	30
Heavy psycannon	30
Hunter-killer missile	6
Hurricane bolter	4
Icarus stormcannon	22
Incinerator	14
Incinerator (Terminator)	20
Krak grenades	0
Las-talon	40
Lascannon	25
Missile launcher	25
Multi-melta	27
Plasma cannon	21
Plasma cutter	7
Psilencer	4
Psilencer (Terminator)	10
Psycannon	14
Psycannon (Terminator)	20
Psyk-out grenades	0
Skyhammer missile launcher	24
Storm bolter	2
Stormstrike missile launcher	21
Twin assault cannon	35
Twin heavy bolter	17
Twin heavy plasma cannon	60
Twin lascannon	50
Twin multi-melta	54
Typhoon missile launcher	50

'Possession was once nine tenths of the lore. It is so even today, but we must blind ourselves to the tenth that remains and was once Human. Duty requires that we put aside such considerations and root out uncleanliness in thought and deed. There can be no other course of action. No one can be adjudged innocent of compliance. Better to self destruct than to acquiesce.'

- The Book of Exorcisms, the Verses of Inquisitor Enoch

MELEE WEAPONS

WEAPON	POINTS PER WEAPON
Crozius arcanum	0
Dreadfist/two Dreadfists	25/35
Dreadnought combat weapon	40
Nemesis Daemon greathammer	15
Nemesis Daemon hammer	13
Nemesis falchion	0
Nemesis force halberd	0
Nemesis force sword	0
Nemesis greatsword	10
Nemesis warding stave	0
Power axe	5
Servo-arm	12

OTHER WARGEAR

WARGEAR	POINTS PER ITEM
Dreadknight teleporter	10

Darkness shrouded the sepulchre, only the wavering light from a handful of sacred candles piercing the gloom. The vaulted ceiling was invisible beyond the candles' glow, the flickering light reflecting from the armour of the Grey Knights who carried them. Six warriors, led by a scarred Brother-Captain in heavily ornamented Terminator armour, made their way through the crypt. On their shoulders, they carried a bier, upon which lay the body of a fallen comrade, his armour removed and flesh purified with cleansing unguents.

The Brother-Captain was named Ceasarian, and carried a Nemesis halberd before him, his voice echoing through the dead air of the tomb as he continued his recital.

'...And on the fields of Charnis did Brother-Captain Ignatius banish a Daemon Prince of the Plague Lord, whose blasphemous name I will not utter, casting him back to the warp for a thousand years and a day.'

A brass-plated skull hovered behind Ceasarian, a feathered quill affixed to a slender mechanical mandible recording his words on a roll of parchment dangling from its lower callipers. Nearly a yard long, the scroll was filled with intricately rendered text.

'The warpcraft of the Decagogue of Panetha Varn was ended on the blade of Brother-Captain Ignatius' divine weapon, and the heretic's soul now burns in the fires of purgation.'

The sombre procession marched in time with the cadence of the captain's words, their helmeted heads betraying no sign of the sorrow they all felt.

At last the Grey Knights approached an open tomb, set within the basalt walls of Titan, the final resting place of Brother-Captain Ignatius.

'The thrice-cursed spawn of the Daemon Broodwomb were wiped from existence by the fires of our captain's will and never more shall its abominable children be allowed to pollute our beloved Emperor's realm with their loathsome visage.'

The Grey Knights lowered the bier and Ceasarian placed Ignatius' Daemon-slaying weapon upon his chest. The Grey Knights slowly began sliding their captain within his tomb as Ceasarian took the gold-edged scroll from the floating skull's callipers and rolled it into a tube, reciting the final verse of the Litany of Heroes. He removed an ivory scroll case from his belt and slid the record of Brother-Captain Ignatius' achievements inside, saying, 'Thus forever more shall the deeds of our fallen brother be set down, that he may carry a fair and true account of his bravery into the next life and take his place at the side of the Emperor.'

Ceasarian placed the sealed scroll tube on Ignatius' chest, making the sign of the Aquila, as the golden door was sealed tight behind their brother. The door's surface was carved with the image of a book pierced by a sword and he stepped back to allow Ignatius' warriors to come forward, each placing a purity seal taken from their own armour upon the door of the tomb as a mark of respect.

Ignatius' battle-brothers marched from the crypt and Ceasarian bowed his head in mourning. One of the greatest heroes of the Imperium was dead, but Ceasarian knew that no one beyond the walls of this fortress monastery would ever learn of his courage.

But Ignatius now stood at the right hand of the Emperor, forever bathed in His eternal grace, and that thought gave Ceasarian solace as he turned and rejoined his warriors.

TACTICAL OBJECTIVES

The tactics employed by the Grey Knights on the battlefield differ significantly from those of other Space Marine Chapters, as the threats they face in their pursuit of Daemons are uniquely challenging.

If your army is led by a Grey Knights Warlord, these Tactical Objectives replace the Capture and Control Tactical Objectives (numbers 11-16) in the *Warhammer 40,000* rulebook. If a mission uses Tactical Objectives, players use the normal rules for using Tactical Objectives with the following exception: when a Grey Knights player generates a Capture and Control objective (numbers 11-16), they instead generate the corresponding Grey Knights Tactical Objective, as shown below. Other Tactical Objectives (numbers 21-66) are generated normally.

D66	TACTICAL OBJECTIVE
11	Destroy the Daemon
12	Psychic Communion
13	No Witnesses!
14	Deeds of Legend
15	Teleport Attack
16	Rites of Exorcism

11 DESTROY THE DAEMON — *Grey Knights*

The daemonic must be destroyed, no matter the cost.

Score 1 victory point if you destroyed at least one enemy Daemon unit during this turn. If you destroyed between 3 and 5 enemy Daemon units during this turn, score D3 victory points instead. If you destroyed 6 or more enemy Daemon units during this turn, score D3+3 victory points instead.

12 PSYCHIC COMMUNION — *Grey Knights*

Utilise the psychic potential of your warriors to defeat your foes.

Score 1 victory point if you successfully manifested at least 3 psychic powers during your turn. If you successfully manifested 6 or more psychic powers during your turn, score D3 victory points instead.

13 NO WITNESSES! — *Grey Knights*

Our existence must be kept a secret; the enemy's leaders cannot be permitted to survive lest they report what they have seen.

Score 1 victory point if all of your opponent's Character models have been removed as casualties.

14 DEEDS OF LEGEND — *Grey Knights*

Though none outside Titan will ever know of it, your deeds and the foes you have slain will not be forgotten.

Score D3 victory points if you killed an enemy Character or Monster during this turn.

15 TELEPORT ATTACK — *Grey Knights*

Teleport into the heart of the battle and annihilate your foe before he can react.

Score 1 victory point if at least one enemy unit was destroyed by a unit in your army that used the Teleport Strike, Personal Teleporters or Warp Emergence ability to arrive on the battlefield this turn, or was the target of the *Gate of Infinity* psychic power this turn.

16 RITES OF EXORCISM — *Grey Knights*

Signs of a warp breach have been detected. Investigate at once and perform the rites to seal it before it can open.

When this Tactical Objective is generated, your opponent must select an objective marker. If you control that objective marker at the end of any turn, score 1 victory point. If you control that objective marker at the end of the turn in which this Tactical Objective was generated, score D3 victory points instead.

'The daemonic leads to two crimes. You turn from the path of righteousness. And you abandon the Emperor as the object of your devotion. For the first, death is merely a just retribution. The second is a heresy so terrible that no punishment can be sufficient. Yet the search for an appropriate penalty continues, and it shall be found.'

- Malleus Daemonicus, the Declaration of Ecclesiarch Issus XLVII